The Mystery of the Creep-Show Crooks

The Three Investigators in

The Three Investigators
in
The Mystery of the Creep-Show Crooks

Text by M. V. Carey
Based on characters created by Robert Arthur

ARMADA

The Mystery of the Creep-Show Crooks
was first published in Armada in 1988.

Armada is an imprint of the Children's Division,
part of the Collins Publishing Group,
8 Grafton Street, London W1X 3LA.

Printed and bound in Great Britain by
William Collins Sons & Co. Ltd, Glasgow.

Contents

A Word from Hector Sebastian

Attention, mystery fans!

The Three Investigators have asked me to introduce their newest adventure. It's a gem – with a cast of characters that could exist only in Hollywood. In Hollywood horror movies, to be exact. There's a werewolf and a ghoul and a girl with a thing for Dracula. The Three Investigators come face to face with all of them – and wish they hadn't!

Before starting this adventure, those of you who haven't already met the Three Investigators might like an introduction. The boys are daring and clever young private eyes who operate in the little California community of Rocky Beach. They have solved some really tough cases, often because they refuse to reject any theories, no matter how bizarre. They also refuse to reject any cases. The company's motto is "We Investigate Anything" and I'm here to tell you those are not empty words.

Jupiter Jones is First Investigator and leader of the group. He's a bit on the chubby side – in fact, some people think he's fat. But behind his moonlike face is an astute brain. Jupiter has a really outstanding ability to sift facts and arrange information so that the answers to puzzles become obvious.

Pete Crenshaw is Second Investigator. He's a tall, athletic boy who is brave, loyal, and willing. He is often called on to do feats of physical daring while the boys are solving a case.

Bob Andrews is in charge of records and research for the group. He is not as strong as Pete, and maybe not as brainy as Jupe, but he is careful and patient. The Three Investigators couldn't operate without him.

That's all I need to say at the moment. The boys will soon speak for themselves when you start the Mystery of the Creep-Show Crooks!

—Hector Sebastian

1

Mystery Beckons

It was Bob Andrews who spotted the plastic tote bag. The bag was half-buried in the sand just above the high-tide line on Rocky Beach. Bob picked it up and looked at it, and had to grin. The bag was the sort of thing that would delight any small girl. Pink pussycats were stencilled on the transparent plastic, and each cat wore a big blue bow. Among the jumble of things inside the bag was a little toy bear. It stared out at Bob with beady black eyes.

"Hey, what tough luck," said Bob. "Some little girl lost her stuff."

His pal, Pete Crenshaw, looked back along the beach. He saw no little girls. It was late and the beach was almost deserted. A lone surfer lugged his board across the sand to the road. The lifeguard was walking away from his watchtower.

"Maybe if we leave the thing here, the kid will remember it and come back," said Pete.

"If she's very young, she probably won't," said the third member of the group, Jupiter Jones. "Besides, someone might steal it."

Jupe – as his friends called him – was a chubby boy with a round, serious face. He had a constructive way of looking at things. "There may be some identification," he said, settling himself on the sand and reaching for the bag. "We may be able to find the little girl."

Bob handed the tote over, and Jupe dumped the contents out into his lap. Then he said, "Hmm!" Then he frowned.

There was no wallet. There was no ID card. There was the small, furry teddy bear, a book called *Success Through Imaging*, a copy of *People* magazine, and all sorts of little tubes and boxes for cosmetics. Jupe counted four different lipsticks, two plastic containers of eye shadow, one for blusher, and an eyeliner pencil. He also saw a pair of purple plastic earrings.

"Not a little girl after all," said Jupiter. "An older girl who wears a lot of make-up."

"And who likes teddy bears," Pete added.

Jupiter flipped through the book that had been in the tote. It was a library book. The manila pocket in the back carried the stamp of the Fresno Public Library.

"Now there's a clue!" said Jupe cheerfully. He loved to solve puzzles. He closed the book and grinned at his friends. "The library will have a record of the borrower. We'll call and find out who it is and restore the tote bag to its owner."

"Call Fresno?" Bob said. Then he shrugged. "Well okay, I guess we can afford a long-distance call."

Pete chuckled. "I bet the girl will be so glad to get her stuff back that she'll pay for the call."

"Or maybe she'll invite us to Fresno to watch the grape harvest," said Jupiter. "Seriously, if we plan to call the Fresno library before it closes, we had better hurry. It's after eight."

The boys started across the sand toward the main road that paralleled the beach. They reclaimed their bikes, waited for a break in the traffic, and then hurried across the road. Without even talking about it they were making for The Jones Salvage Yard.

The salvage yard was something of a landmark in Rocky Beach. It was owned by Jupiter's uncle and aunt, Titus and Mathilda Jones, with whom the orphaned Jupiter lived. The yard held a wonderful collection of used items – everything from old pipes and washing machines to antique doorknobs and carousel horses. Jupe felt that the name 'junk' was unworthy of the yard's merchandise, and he had convinced his aunt and uncle to improve the place's image by calling it The Jones Salvage Yard instead of The Jones Junkyard.

By the time the boys reached the yard this evening, it was growing dark. The big iron gates were closed and padlocked. Across the street, the windows of the Jones house were golden squares of light.

The boys ignored the house. They rode past the gates to the far corner of the yard.

The wooden fence that enclosed the yard was wildly

decorated. Artists who lived in Rocky Beach often got items from Uncle Titus at reduced prices, since Uncle Titus believed in encouraging talent. The artists had thanked him by banding together to spend a hilarious weekend painting pictures on his fence. On the front was a green lake where swans swam and also a green ocean where a sailing ship battled a terrible storm. In the midst of the green waves, a painted fish watched the sinking vessel.

The fish's eye was actually a knothole in the fence. Jupe put his hand on this now and pushed. Two boards swung up. This was Green Gate One, one of the secret ways into the yard. All of them had been devised by Jupe and his friends so that they could come and go without being seen by Aunt Mathilda or Uncle Titus.

The boys went through the opening and were immediately in Jupiter's outdoor workshop. It was an area set off from the rest of the yard by partitions of junk. Jupe moved an iron grating that seemed to be leaning against the bottom of his workbench. Then he bent and crawled into the large galvanized iron pipe that had been concealed by the grating.

This was Tunnel Two, another of the secret passages that the boys had rigged up. Pete and Bob followed Jupe into the pipe, which went through piles of junk and ended under a trap door. This admitted the boys into the old mobile home trailer that was their special territory.

The trailer had been badly banged up in an accident, and Uncle Titus had bought it as salvage. When months had passed with no offer for it, he had finally given the trailer to Jupiter and his friends to use as a clubhouse.

But the trailer had not become a clubhouse. Instead, Jupe, Pete, and Bob had outfitted it with a desk, a filing cabinet, a small crime laboratory, and a darkroom. They had also installed a telephone, which they paid for with money they earned doing odd jobs in the yard. And, while working, they carefully piled junk around the trailer until it was hidden from view.

When the trailer was ready, the boys had gone into business. Calling themselves The Three Investigators and calling the trailer Headquarters, they had set about solving mysteries – great ones and small ones. The lost tote bag was giving Jupe a thrill of excitement now. Starting to work on a new puzzle always excited him.

Inside Headquarters, Jupe called directory enquiries in Fresno. He got the telephone number of the public library there and dialled it.

"Twenty to nine," said Pete, looking at the clock on top of the filing cabinet. "You don't have much time to get the information."

It did not take much time. Jupe was switched to the circulation desk immediately.

"Jupiter Jones calling." He managed to sound important as he told the woman there the reason for his call.

"We have our circulation records on the computer," the librarian answered. "I'll see what I can do."

She left the phone for a moment. When she returned there was tension in her voice.

"Can I call you back?" she said." Are you at a number where I can reach you?"

"Well, yes, but – "

"Please!" urged the woman.

Jupe gave her the telephone number.

"Okay," she said. "Now stay where you are. Don't leave the phone."

She hung up.

Jupe put down the receiver. "Now, what was that all about?" he wondered. "That woman was very upset. She said she would call back."

"Good grief," Pete said. "What are we getting into?"

The call came within minutes. The voice at the other end of the line was high with hysteria.

"Have you seen her?" demanded the caller. It was a woman, but not the librarian Jupe had just spoken to. "I'm coming. Wherever you are, I'm coming. I have to find my little girl!"

2

Runaway!

A loudspeaker sat on the desk. Jupe had put it together, using parts of salvaged electronics equipment that he had found in the yard. When he placed the telephone receiver on the gadget, all three boys could hear the conversation.

What they heard now was weeping. Then a man's voice said, "Judy, for Pete's sake, don't do that!"

Someone fumbled with the telephone. The man spoke into the receiver. "Jupiter Jones?" he said.

"Yes?" said Jupe.

"You found a library book on the beach?"

"Yes, sir."

"My daughter borrowed that book from the Fresno Public Library just before she disappeared."

"Oh," said Jupe.

"You see, she ran off to Hollywood to get into the movies."

In the background the woman said, "Tell him we're coming."

"Okay, Judy. Okay."

The man took a deep breath. "My name is Charles Anderson. Your telephone call is the first real sign we've had that Lucille is probably okay. We have to see you. Maybe we can find out something. I don't suppose there was an address in her tote bag?"

"No, Mr Anderson," Jupe told him. "No address."

"The police haven't been a lot of help," continued Mr Anderson. "They keep saying there are too many runaways in Los Angeles. So if you'll give me your address, we'll be there in the morning."

"Yes, sir," Jupe agreed. He gave the address of the salvage yard.

Anderson thanked him and hung up.

"A missing daughter!" Pete exclaimed. "That could be a

really big case for The Three Investigators!"

Jupe was paging through the book from the Fresno library. "Whether or not we can assist the Andersons, let's hope the girl turns up soon. If I'm not mistaken, these slips of paper she's been using for bookmarks are pawn tickets. This one's from the Hi-Lo Loan and Jewellery Company. And here's one from Cash-in-a-Flash, Inc. It would seem that the girl is broke."

Jupe closed the book and stared at its title. "*Success Through Imaging*," he read. "I've heard of this book. According to the author you can be a success just by imagining yourself in an important job or an expensive house or . . ."

"Or a starring role in a movie?" Bob finished.

"I suppose so," said Jupe. He opened the book at random and began to read: "'Forget about using willpower. Willpower is concerned with details, and details will only get in your way. Instead of working and worrying, project yourself into a future rich with success. This is the great secret. Feel the success, not as something that might happen someday, but as something that is happening right now.'"

Jupe closed the book.

"Too much!" Pete observed. Grinning, the Investigators left the trailer and headed home.

The next morning all three boys were waiting near the office of the salvage yard when a Toyota pulled in and the driver got out and asked to see Jupiter Jones. He was a tall, spare man with receding brown hair and an intelligent-looking face. A dark-haired woman with a very anxious expression was getting out of the passenger seat. Her slightly matronly look was offset by her elaborately styled bouffant hairdo.

"Mr Anderson?" said Jupe.

"Yes. I'm Anderson. You're the one who found Lucille's tote bag?"

"Yes, sir. I'm Jupiter Jones." Jupe then introduced Pete and Bob. Aunt Mathilda, who had heard about the missing girl, came out of the office and invited the Andersons inside to talk.

The tote was on the desk in the office. When Mr Anderson saw it he nodded. "That's the sort of thing Lucille loves to carry around," he said. He spilled the contents out onto the desk, stared at the make-up and teddy bear, and then made a face. "Doesn't tell us much," he said.

Mrs Anderson had picked up the library book and found the pawn tickets.

"Charles, she's starving!" Mrs Anderson declared. "She's probably out on the street with the criminals and the tramps! Anything could happen to her!"

She handed a pawn ticket to Mr Anderson. He glanced at it and for a moment looked really grim. Then he put the ticket down and said firmly, "People have been known to pawn things even when they weren't out on the street with the tramps. Don't borrow trouble."

He had brought a manila envelope from the car. He turned this upside down and a torrent of photographs spilled out on the desk.

"This is Lucille," said Mr Anderson. He held a snapshot out to the boys. "She's sixteen years old. If you go to the beach a lot you might have seen her."

Jupiter and his friends passed the pictures from hand to hand. They showed a pretty, dark-haired girl with green-brown eyes. In one photo she was wearing a drum majorette's costume and too much lipstick. Other photos showed her dressed as a ballet dancer and as a pilgrim. They had been taken following church pageants. There were pictures of Lucille aged ten, and then aged thirteen when she was named runner-up in the Miss Teen Fresno contest.

After seeing all the photos, the boys were more puzzled than before.

"She . . . she seems so different in the different shots," said Pete. "It's hard to tell what she really looks like."

"That's because she keeps fiddling with her hair-style and face," said Mr Anderson. "Long hair, short hair. White lipstick, dark red, orange. I think the only colour I haven't seen is green. Or blue. She never wears blue lipstick. And she hadn't got around to dyeing her hair before she left home."

Mrs Anderson began to cry.

15

"We keep calling the police departments in the area," said Mr Anderson, "and they keep giving us the line they probably give to all the parents. I guess it isn't their fault, but we can't just wait for Lucille to turn up. She might be in danger. We have to start somewhere. I want to see the place where you found the tote bag on the beach, and I want to talk to the lifeguards."

Jupe nodded, and he and his friends piled into the Andersons' car. They spent the rest of the morning watching Mr and Mrs Anderson trudge up and down the beach, talking to lifeguards and to the young sunbathers. By one o'clock the Andersons were exhausted and discouraged.

"Nobody recognizes the pictures," muttered Mr Anderson.

"She's prettier than her pictures," said Mrs Anderson. "That's the trouble."

Mr Anderson glared. "If you hadn't kept telling her that, none of this would have happened," he said.

Mrs Anderson began to cry again.

"Look, I'm sorry," said her husband. "I didn't mean that. We'll find her."

He turned to the boys. "How long would it take us to really check out this town? We could knock on doors and put up signs in supermarkets. We could mail handbills to everybody who lives here. Or we could run ads in the paper!"

"Maybe you should talk to Chief Reynolds," Bob suggested. "He's the police chief here in Rocky Beach and he's a pretty nice guy."

So Mr Anderson drove into the centre of town to the police station. Chief Reynolds listened to the story of Lucille, who had saved her babysitting money to run away to Hollywood.

The chief sighed when Mr Anderson finished his tale. "We get too many of these kids," he said. He thumbed through the photographs and nodded. "She's pretty, all right. May I keep a picture?"

"Certainly," Mrs Anderson told him.

"When did you hear from her last?" said the chief.

"Two months ago," Judy Anderson replied. "That was two days after she left home. She phoned and told us not to worry, but she hung up before we could say much."

Chief Reynolds nodded. He wrote down the Andersons' address and telephone number. "I'll have my people keep an eye out," he promised. "Meanwhile, the boys here might take an interest – if they haven't done so already."

Mr Anderson was startled. "The boys? These boys? They've been very obliging, to be sure, but what . . .?"

"They're amateur detectives," said Chief Reynolds. There was no hint of mockery in his voice. "They have a detective agency and they investigate problems and unusual events of all kinds. They get in my way and sometimes drive me nuts, but they do seem to have a real knack for finding things out. And they keep working on a problem until they find the solution. These guys also go to the beach a lot, and if your daughter likes the beach . . ."

Chief Reynolds did not finish the sentence. He just watched as Jupe took out his wallet and handed a card to Mr Anderson. It was the business card of the Three Investigators, which said:

THE THREE INVESTIGATORS
"We Investigate Anything"
? ? ?

First Investigator .... Jupiter Jones
Second Investigator .... Peter Crenshaw
Records and Research .... Bob Andrews

Mr Anderson studied the card for a second, then said, "Why not? No one else has found out anything. Would you boys like a cheque?"

"That won't be necessary," said Jupe. "If we are able to locate Lucille, we can submit a bill for any expenses we might incur. All we need right now is a photo of your daughter."

"Anything you say," declared Mr Anderson, handing Jupe the whole envelope. "If you need anything, just call me. Transfer the charges."

"What do we do now?" Mrs Anderson asked Chief Reynolds sadly.

"Go back to Fresno," he said. "Sit by the telephone. Your daughter might call. We'll let you know if we learn anything."

"My poor baby," Mrs Anderson said in a choked voice. "What if we never see her again?"

3

The Hollywood Werewolf

"Did you get what the chief said?" crowed Pete. "He practically recommended us. Unreal!"

Bob scowled at the photographs spread out on the desk in Headquarters. He had the day off from his part-time job at the Rocky Beach library. "Yeah, it was great," he said. "Only where do we start? There must be hundreds of kids who run away to Hollywood."

Jupiter's smile was a bit superior. "Shall we start with the pawnshops?" he said.

Bob sat up straighter. "Oh, of course!"

"Uncle Titus travelled with a circus when he was younger," said Jupe, "and he was often short of money. He knows about pawnshops. He says that when you borrow money from a pawnbroker, you let him hold something of value as security for the loan, and you have to give him your name and address."

"Oh, wow!" Pete was jubilant. "We're home free!"

"We are if those are Lucille Anderson's pawn tickets in the book," Jupe replied, "and if she gave the pawnbrokers her real name and address. If she didn't, those tickets are just the beginning.

"All of these tickets are from shops in the Hollywood area. Konrad is driving in to Hollywood in a little while and we can hitch a ride with him. We'll find out very quickly how useful the tickets are as clues."

Konrad was one of two Bavarian brothers who did the heavy hauling and lifting in the junkyard. He was waiting in the drive near the office when the boys hurried out. He had heard the tale of the runaway girl and the anxious parents and was all sympathy. Although he was really going to Hollywood to pick up a load of used timber, he gladly took a detour to the first pawnshop.

Jupiter, Pete, and Bob piled out of the lorry and went

into the shop. It was a dim place with a musty smell. The pawnbroker glanced at the ticket that Jupe presented to him, then turned away and opened a locked cupboard. He took out a little silver medal on a blue ribbon. "Are you going to redeem it?" he asked, handing it to Jupe.

There was a design on the front of the medal that looked a bit like the Statue of Liberty. On the back was an inscription announcing that Lucille Anderson had taken third place in the Fresno Jaycees' Spelling Bee.

"The girl who pawned this," said Jupe. "What address did she give? We're friends of her parents."

"A runaway?" guessed the pawnbroker.

"Yes. She's been gone for two months and . . ."

The man raised a hand to stop Jupe. "Don't tell me," he said. "It's an old story. They come here to get famous and they get broke instead."

He flipped through a card file on the counter. "What name did you say?"

"Lucille Anderson," said Jupe.

The man shook his head. "Nope. Somebody named Valerie Cargill pawned that thing."

"Valerie Cargill?" Bob echoed it. "You're kidding!"

"I have no sense of humour," said the man. "I never kid."

"Is there an address?" Jupiter asked.

He looked again at the file. "West Los Angeles," he told them. "1648 Riverside Drive."

"There's no Riverside Drive in West Los Angeles," Bob announced.

"That figures," said the pawnbroker. He took the picture that Jupe held out to him. When he inspected it, his expression softened. "Nice-looking kid. Isn't much like the one who pawned the medal. I remember that one. She was blonde, with a mole on her cheek. A beauty mark, I guess. She looked like that girl on the night-time soap opera – *Triumph!* My wife watches it every Monday."

"That actress is Valerie Cargill," said Jupe.

The pawnbroker nodded. "I'm not surprised. And it doesn't take a genius to know it wasn't the real Valerie

20

Cargill who pawned that pathetic little medal. Look . . . are you going to redeem it? It'll cost you eight dollars and seventy cents."

Jupe paid the man and took the medal. The boys went back to the lorry.

"I thought this case would be a cinch," complained Pete.

"We have to keep trying," said Jupe. "One of the pawnbrokers may give us a real lead."

At the second pawnshop the broker was obliging enough, but he could not give the boys any really useful information. A girl had come in to pawn a gold baby ring. She had been wearing a tunic and knee-high boots and strongly resembled a character in the space thriller *Search for Erehwon*.

"What name did she use?" asked Jupiter.

"Allida Cantrell," said the broker.

"That was the name of the lead actress in the space adventure."

The boys left the gold ring behind, since they did not have enough money to redeem it. They went back to the lorry and found Konrad eating an apple and worrying about the time.

"I like to help Jupe," he said, "only your aunt Mathilda says not to take all day."

"We won't take much more of your time, Konrad. We promise," said Jupe. "There's only one more pawnshop. It's over on Hollywood Boulevard."

Konrad scowled, but he drove to Hollywood Boulevard. "I do not like this street," he announced.

The Investigators could see why. It was a very shabby neighbourhood. A bag lady was poking in the rubbish bin on a corner, and seedy-looking people drifted along the street. Nowhere did the boys see any sign of the supposed glamour of Hollywood.

There was a parking place at the kerb, a block beyond the pawnshop. Konrad pulled into it and the boys got out of the lorry and went back. They passed a little store selling souvenirs of Hollywood and maps of the stars' homes. The pawnshop was two doors beyond that. Pete was in the lead as they approached the place.

"What a waste of time," he complained.

21

Then there was a shout from inside the pawnshop. A figure bounded out and elbowed Pete aside.

"Hey!" Pete yelled. "Watch it, huh!"

The person who had run from the shop turned back and reached towards Pete. Pete stared at him. He saw a face that was dark and leathery. He saw pointed teeth – teeth like fangs. He saw a broad nose and wide, flaring nostrils. He could not see the eyes. They were sunken in the head – hidden, as evil things often are.

Pete opened his mouth to shout again, but no sound came out. He looked down at the hands that clutched him. They were claws, dark and furry.

Someone yelled inside the pawnshop. The nightmare being let go of Pete and plunged away.

For a second no one moved. Then the man in the pawnshop shouted, "Stop that guy!"

On the pavement a woman screamed.

The fleeing horror disappeared into the souvenir store. Again there were screams.

Pete pulled himself together and started after the creature, but it was too late. The fugitive was out through the back of the store, down the alley, and away.

The boys returned to the pawnshop to question the shaken owner.

"Hey, that guy tried to rob me!" the man exclaimed. "When he saw you boys coming, he got scared off!"

In moments there were sirens on the boulevard. A squad car pulled up in front of the pawnshop, and then a second one. A crowd gathered. The boys came out of the pawnshop, followed by the proprietor, who was gesturing wildly.

One of the officers moved the crowd back. A second one talked to the pawnbroker, who pointed at Pete. A third officer turned to the boy.

"You the one who tried to stop the guy?" asked the police officer.

Pete nodded.

"What happened?" said the officer.

Pete hesitated. "You're going to think I'm some kind of a nut," he said.

"Try me," the officer prompted.

"He looked like . . . like a monster!"

The officer nodded patiently. "Would that be like a gorilla?" he said calmly. "Or was it some other kind of monster?"

"Well, yes. I mean, no. Not a gorilla exactly. More like a – a werewolf!"

"Hmm," said the officer. He wrote in a notebook. "How tall was the werewolf?" he continued.

"About my height," Pete told him. "Kind of chunky."

The officer then turned to Jupiter. "And what exactly did you see?" he asked.

Jupe said that he too had seen a werewolf.

"Officer, you don't seem at all surprised by our story," Jupiter noted.

The police officer grinned. "That's because some guy dressed as a gorilla held up a gas station last week," he said.

"Yeah, now I remember seeing it in the papers," put in the pawnbroker. "And wasn't there one crook with a green face and a bolt sticking out of his neck? He held up an off licence on Santa Monica."

One of the officers smiled. "Nothing is ordinary in this town."

After the police had left, the pawnbroker said to the boys, "You were coming to see me?"

Jupe told him about Lucille. The man led the way into his shop and dived into his records. Then he opened a drawer and took out a delicate little gold pin that was shaped like a bow.

"Hate to see anybody pawn a thing like this," said the pawnbroker. "It's the kind of pin people give a girl when she graduates from grade school."

"Do you remember the girl who pawned it?" said Jupe. "Was it this girl?"

He held out a photograph of Lucille Anderson. The pawnbroker took it and studied it for a moment. "Could be. She was wearing make-up an inch thick, and her hair was lighter, but it could be."

He went back to his records and announced that the pin had been pawned by someone called Juliette Ravenna.

"That's the name of an actress," groaned Jupe. "We are at a dead end!"

4

The Girl with a Thousand Faces

The boys met at Headquarters that evening. Pete sat on the floor and scowled. "How can we find a kid who looks different every day?"

For a few moments no one had an answer. Then Jupe ventured a plan.

"If Lucille Anderson is serious about getting into films, she might have made the rounds of the theatrical agencies. We can do the same thing."

"We can try," said Pete. "What have we got to lose?"

Early the next morning the boys caught a bus into Hollywood. They began at the top of a list that Jupe had prepared. The receptionist there was a very thin young woman who would not listen to them at all.

"We don't discuss clients with anyone," she said primly.

"But – but she may not be a client," Pete blurted out.

"I'm much too busy to play games with you boys," the receptionist retorted, and she went back to her typing.

At the second agency the receptionist gave the boys a reproving look when they asked about Lucille.

"If I did know her, I wouldn't tell you," she said. "Shame on you! You're too young to be chasing actresses."

Jupiter felt his face get red. "We aren't chasing actresses," he said. "The young lady's parents have asked us to help find her and –"

"A missing juvenile?" interrupted the woman. "Then her parents should go to the police. And we don't sign up runaway kids. They're just trouble looking for a place to happen."

At the third agency the receptionist was more cordial, possibly because she recognized Jupiter's name.

"You're Baby Fatso!" she cried.

It was a reference to Jupe's early career as a child

performer. Jupe hated to admit that he had once been a chubby child TV star. The mere mention of Baby Fatso was enough to start him dieting. He scowled now and took out a picture of Lucille Anderson.

The receptionist looked at the picture and shook her head. "Looks like a lot of other kids," she said. "Who is she? Your sister? A friend?"

Jupe gave the woman one of the cards of The Three Investigators. "Her name is Lucille Anderson," he explained. "Her parents have asked us to try to find her. She left home two months ago."

"You're probably wasting your time," said the receptionist. "She's one of thousands of kids like that. But if she's trying to get into show business, there is one outside chance. She might try to audition for the television programme *Reach for a Star*. They really do give amateurs a chance to go on the air."

The woman gave the boys the address of the studio where the auditions were held. The boys thanked her and hurried off. When they got to the studio they saw a line of young hopefuls stretching down the block and around the corner.

Jupe made an impatient noise and tried to go directly to the studio entrance. Shouts of protest went up from the people in the line.

Pete grabbed Jupe by the arm. "There's got to be a better way! We could spend the rest of our lives standing in that line."

Jupe sat down on a bus bench. "We have to get an edge somehow," he said glumly.

But then he brightened. "We'll do a mailing! It's what Mr Anderson wanted to do in Rocky Beach. But we'll do it with the talent agents. We'll have handbills printed with Lucille's description and a picture or two. We'll mail one to every agent and every studio in town, and we'll ask if anyone who has seen Lucille will call The Three Investigators."

He looked eagerly at Pete and Bob. "Dignified," Jupe said. "Simple. We put no one on the defensive."

"I like it," said Bob.

"I like anything better than slogging all over Hollywood

trying to talk to people who don't want to talk to us," said Pete.

The boys felt happier as they rode the bus home to Rocky Beach. At the salvage yard they found that Konrad's brother, Hans, had been left in charge. Uncle Titus and Aunt Mathilda had gone on a buying trip to Ventura, where a whole block of old buildings was being renovated. "Your aunt says she did not get to the supermarket yet, so there is nothing in the refrigerator for you to eat," Hans told Jupiter. "She says if you are hungry you should take money from the china teapot and get something you like, like pizza."

"Hey, that's all right!" said Pete. "Want some company?"

Bob was digging in his pocket. "My mom isn't expecting me back till late," he said.

"Fine," said Jupe. "We can draft the handbill while we eat. Or at least we can talk it over. Is the Pizza Shack okay with you guys?"

It was, and the three biked there in a few minutes.
The Pizza Shack was a popular hangout on the Coast Highway in Rocky Beach. Teenagers came there to eat pizza, play the video games, listen to music, and see their friends.

When the three boys arrived that day, at least a dozen young people were clustered around a video game. They were watching and cheering as a girl with masses of dark hair piled on her head played the game, bobbing back and forth as she worked the joysticks.

Bob, Pete, and Jupe ordered a large pepperoni pizza at the counter, then sat down to wait. A cheer went up from the kids around the video game.

"That girl must be good," Bob observed.

But then the game ended. The teenagers laughed and the girl turned away from the machine. She was laughing too. The others stepped aside to make way for her. She started for the door, and as she crossed the room the three boys at the table saw that her skirts were long enough to brush the ground. She wore an old-fashioned blouse with a ruffle down the front. Her earrings dangled, and there was a tiny

27

watch pinned to the front of her blouse. With her sweet, demure expression, her upswept hair, and her old-fashioned clothes, she looked like a girl from the last century. She smiled quickly at the three boys, then went out to the main road.

"What's she all dressed up for?" Bob wondered. "She looks like she's got a part in a play or something."

A plump woman came from the kitchen carrying a tray loaded with food. She put a big pizza in the middle of the boys' table and went off to get their soft drinks.

Jupe began to separate a slice of pizza from the plate in front of him. Suddenly he stopped, the piece falling back into a sea of cheese. "That was her!" he exclaimed.

"What?" asked Pete.

"It was her! Lucille Anderson! It was her!"

Jupiter raced to the door, snatched it open, and shot out into the parking lot in front of the Pizza Shack. He looked left and right and then across the main road. He saw cars speeding past, and a few pedestrians on the far side of the road. But the girl with the old-fashioned clothes was gone!

5

A New Lead

"Hold it a second, everybody!" Jupiter shouted. "It's important!" The First Investigator had returned to the Pizza Shack and was trying to get the attention of the video game players. He stood as tall as he could and looked very serious. The players stopped their game and turned toward Jupe, surprised. The waitress froze in her tracks on her way into the kitchen.

"We've been trying to find the girl who just left here," said Jupe.

The others glanced at one another. They were suspicious and uneasy now. "Why?" said one of them.

Jupe took out the pictures of Lucille Anderson and began to hand them around. "Lucille Anderson's parents gave us these pictures," he said. "They asked us to try to find her. She's from Fresno, and she's been missing from home for two months."

"That kid's name isn't Anderson," said one of the boys. "It isn't Lucille, either."

"She may be using another name," Bob suggested.

"You guys have been seeing too many spy movies," said one of the girls.

Pete said hotly, "No, we haven't! Look, her mum's about to go off her rocker. How would your mum feel if you just . . . just disappeared?"

The others looked uncomfortable. One girl said, "That girl isn't a runaway. She lives around here."

"Are you sure?" said Bob. "Have you known her long?"

"A while," she said.

"More than two months?" Jupe and his friends had the others on the defensive now. No one answered. "She likes to dress up in different costumes, doesn't she? And she changes her hair colour, too."

29

There was silence in the Pizza Shack. The video game players looked at one another, unwilling to say any more. Who were these three guys anyway?

Just then a maroon Audi pulled up outside and a grey-haired man came into the restaurant.

"Why is it so quiet in here?" said the man. "Trouble?"

"Everything's fine, Mr Sears," said the waitress. "This boy here is just looking for a friend."

Mr Sears grunted and walked behind the counter. Apparently he was the manager, for he opened the cash register and began counting the money.

One of the girls spoke to Jupe at last. "That girl who was here, she lives up on the main road in that place that looks like it's really old – Cheshire Square. Her name's Arianne."

"Arianne what?" Bob asked.

"Ardis. Arianne Ardis."

Jupe snorted. "You really think that's her name?"

"Why shouldn't it be?" said one of the boys. "And if that kid ran away, why did she do it? There's always a reason when someone runs away. Her old lady's been giving her a hard time or –"

"She wants to be a movie star," interrupted Pete. "That's why she did it. Nobody's been giving her a hard time. At least we don't think so."

"Okay," said the boy. "When we see her again we'll tell her you're looking for her. Does that satisfy you?"

Jupe hesitated. Then he took out one of The Three Investigators' cards and wrote down the telephone number of Headquarters. "Ask her to call," he said, and he handed the card to the boy.

The boy glanced at it and grinned. "Junior private eyes, huh?" He tucked the card into the pocket of his jeans. "Okay, kid, we'll tell her."

Jupe thanked him and returned to his pizza.

The waitress went back into the kitchen, followed by the grey-haired manager, and the players went back to their game.

Bob leaned close to Jupe. "Do you really think that girl is going to call us?"

"No," mumbled Jupe through a mouthful of cold pizza. "But we don't have to wait for her to call us, do we? If she lives in Cheshire Square, we know how to find her. Eat up. It may be a long afternoon."

Cheshire Square looked old, but it was not. The development of homes had been completed less than a year before. It stood on a bluff overlooking the Pacific. The complex sparkled with fresh paint, gleaming brass, and new lawns and flower beds.

The builder who had developed Cheshire Square was a visionary with a sense of humour. In a newspaper interview he had said that he wanted to confuse the archaeologists of the future. "Someday they'll dig up the remains of an 1890s house," he had said. "They'll find it chock-full of high-tech improvements that didn't come along until a hundred years later. It will totally confuse them!"

And so the houses he had built were decorated with gables and turrets and the wooden gingerbread trim typical of Victorian homes. He also added verandas and attics and cellars. The houses were ringed by formal gardens with wrought-iron fences and summer houses. And in the centre of the development there was a tiny park with an old-fashioned bandstand.

The boys could see the bandstand from the gatehouse where a uniformed guard kept watch.

"No Lucille Anderson here," said the guard.

"How about Arianne Ardis?" said Jupiter.

The man's face grew stern. "Does she know you?"

"Certainly," replied Jupiter.

"Your names?" the man demanded.

"Jupiter Jones!" declared Jupe. "This is Bob Andrews and that's Pete Crenshaw. We're friends of Mr and Mrs Charles Anderson of Fresno, and we have an important message for Arianne."

The guard hesitated, his hand on his telephone.

"If you'll call and announce us," said Jupiter, "you'll find that she'll be delighted. Friends of Mr and Mrs Anderson. Be sure to tell her that."

But the guard was not listening. A siren wailed on the main road below. It was a police car, and it was coming fast.

The boys turned to look down the road that connected Cheshire Square with the Coast Highway. They saw a car from the Rocky Beach Police Department moving so fast that it skidded when it turned off the main road.

It roared up the gate toward the gatehouse.

Someone inside the housing complex screamed. It was a high-pitched scream, shrill with fright and anger.

"Watch out!" yelled Bob.

The gateman had stepped out of his little house. He was directly in the path of the man who came racing out of the square of Victorian houses. The man ran with his head down and his arms pumping. The Three Investigators saw only dark hair and a dark shirt. Then the fleeing man lifted his head as the guard tried to stop him, and the boys saw that he had pulled a pair of tights over his head. His features were flattened and distorted.

The gateman dove for his legs but the fugitive dodged and punched him. The gateman went down and rolled over in the road. Jupe and Bob leaped to his aid.

Pete jumped, trying to get in the masked man's path, to stop him as he fled. The runner struck out again with his fist. Pete felt his teeth snap together as the blow landed.

Pete staggered back and sat down hard. The dark figure crashed into the underbrush, leaping and scrambling straight down the hillside. In a second he was gone!

6

A Terrifying Surprise

The patrol car pulled up. Two police officers jumped out and went crashing down the hill in pursuit of the fleeing man. Suddenly a second police car arrived and two more officers climbed out. One began helping the gateman to his feet. Another bent over Pete, who was still on the ground, gingerly feeling his chin.

"Are you okay?" said the officer. "Can you stand up? We'll take you to the emergency room."

"I'm fine," said Pete. "Just so long as my teeth don't fall out."

Pete got to his feet and leaned against the gatehouse.

Then he saw the girl – the old-fashioned girl with the long skirt and the ruffled blouse. She was talking frantically to the officer who had tried to help Pete.

"He broke in!" said the girl. "He had to! How else would that burglar be there? I was just coming in. I went upstairs and was halfway down the hall when I knew somebody was there."

The girl's face was ghastly white and she was trembling. The guard limped to his little house and brought out his chair so she could sit down.

"Which house?" said the officer. "Where do you live?"

The girl gestured back towards the little park. Suddenly she shook her head and began to cry.

"It's the Fowler place," said the guard. He pointed across the square. "There," he said. "Number fourteen. Just the other side of the park."

The officer nodded, and he and his partner got into their car and drove up the street. The girl in the long skirt stayed where she was. Jupiter and his friends watched her. Her face was thinner than the face in the Andersons' photographs but her eyes did look greenish-brown. Was it Lucille Anderson? Or was it just a look-alike who also

33

enjoyed wearing costumes instead of ordinary clothes?

In a short time the patrol car returned, and the policemen who had run down the slope after the burglar came trudging back, looking hot and unhappy. The officer who had first talked to the girl now crouched beside her chair.

"Would you feel up to helping us now?" said the officer. "Could you go back to the house with us and see if anything is missing?"

She nodded and began to stand up. But then she sat down suddenly.

"It's okay," said the police officer. "Take your time."

"When I heard him," she began, "I was halfway down the hall, and he was behind me somewhere – not in the hall. He was in one of the bedrooms, and I would have had to pass him to get to the stairs. I just . . . just couldn't."

Her voice broke, and the boys imagined the terror of that moment, when the girl realized there was an intruder between herself and freedom.

She cleared her throat and went on. "I went into Mrs Fowler's room and closed the door, like I hadn't noticed anything. I put a chair under the doorknob and turned on the radio, then I called the police on the telephone next to the bed."

"Right," said the officer. "You've a brave, level-headed young lady. What then?"

"Then nothing. I mean, I just waited for the police. But then when I heard the sirens at the bottom of the hill, and I heard the burglar running down the stairs, all of a sudden I was just so mad! I didn't want him to get away so I ran too – after him!"

The officer nodded. "Not the wisest course. Luckily the guy kept on running."

She stood up. "I'm okay now," she said. "We can go back to the house."

But the guard was not satisfied with this. "You should have someone stay with you," he said. "Why don't you call some of your friends?"

She shook her head. "My friends are . . . out of town."

Jupe stepped forward. "We could call your mother, Lucille," he said softly.

She flinched. Then she turned coolly to Jupiter. "Lucille? My name isn't Lucille," she said. "My name is Arianne."

"Don't upset her!" snapped the guard. "Can't you see she's had a scare?"

She got into the patrol car and was driven into Cheshire Square while one of the other officers took names, addresses, and statements from the boys. The statements would probably not be very helpful. The fleeing man had been of medium height, was dark-haired, and had worn dark clothing. That was all they knew for certain.

Eventually the second patrol car drove away. The gate-man looked at the bruise blooming on Pete's cheek and shook his head. "Bunch of thugs we've got roaming around these days," he said. "Not right for a kid like her to be alone in that big house – not after a burglar got in."

"What about the people who own the place?" asked Bob. "Where are they?"

"Mrs Jamison Fowler is in Europe," said the man. "She left a few days ago. Arianne's been with her for a few weeks now. Mrs Fowler's a really nice lady. Sometimes she takes in kids like this one who are having a hard time living on their own. She sees that they've got a nice room and enough to eat and somebody to keep an eye on them. Arianne's got a part-time job somewhere. Here in the Square she's been doing some chores for Mrs. Fowler and keeping the housekeeper company, but the housekeeper was called home yesterday for some kind of family emergency."

He paused and looked at the boys in a speculative way. "You think you know her?"

Jupe showed the pictures of Lucille Anderson to the guard. "Lucille Anderson's parents gave these to us," he said. "What do you think?"

The security man went through the pictures slowly. His expression did not change, but when he finished he said, "I have a daughter that age myself."

"If it was your daughter," said Jupe, "wouldn't you want to know that she was okay?"

35

The man nodded. "I'll talk to her and see if she will see you. Maybe she is your missing person. Only this isn't the best time, after that fright she had, and with the police here."

"Suppose we come back in the morning," said Jupe.

"Fine. Meanwhile I'll talk to Arianne, and maybe I can persuade her to stay at home tomorrow – or at least not to go to work until you get here."

Jupiter came alone to Cheshire Square the next day. He and Pete and Bob had decided that only one of them should confront the girl in the Fowler house.

"We don't want it to look as if we're bullying her," Bob had pointed out. "Three against one would sure look like bullying."

So it was Jupe who found the gateman waiting for him. "I didn't say anything about her parents wanting you to find her," the guard told him. "She's probably figured that one out for herself anyway. I just told her you and your friends wanted to be sure she was okay. She said she'd see you."

The gateman pointed out the Fowler house. "That big one, just the other side of the park."

Jupe thanked him and went through the gate. He walked up to number 14, a two-storey building bedecked with turrets, fancy shutters, and wooden curlicues. As he approached the house, the girl who called herself Arianne opened the door and came out on to the porch. "Hi!" she said. "I was watching for you."

"Jupiter Jones," said Jupe, extending his hand.

Laughing with embarrassment, the girl shook hands briefly, then turned to go inside. Jupe followed her. Immediately he felt that he had stepped into another age. The entrance hall was lofty, with a wide staircase going up to a gallery on the second floor. There were a lot of ferns and dark wood panelling. Thick red carpeting muffled their footsteps and paintings glistened in heavy gilt frames.

"Creepy, isn't it?" said the girl to Jupe. "Come on out to the kitchen. It's nicer there."

Jupe followed her past the stairs. They went through a pantry into a big sunny kitchen. A kettle boiled on a stove that looked old-fashioned but which was actually electric.

The girl motioned to Jupe to sit at the round table between two windows. As she poured drinks for them – tea for her and ginger ale for Jupiter – he sat quietly and watched her. She was wearing a gown that trailed ruffles on the floor. A ribbon tied her long hair back from her delicate heart-shaped face with its small, determined chin. More than ever she looked quaint and old-fashioned. Jupe realized she was dressed to match the house.

"It's great that Mrs Fowler lets you stay here," Jupiter began.

"It certainly is," the girl agreed. "Mrs Fowler has been really nice to me."

"How did you get to know her?" asked Jupe.

"Well, you know, I have this job at the Tender Touch Beauty Salon."

Jupiter nodded, recognizing the name of a beauty parlour in Rocky Beach.

"It's actually a stupid job," the girl went on. "I sweep up after haircuts. But other actresses have done worse before they got their breaks. So anyway, Mrs Fowler comes in often to get her hair done and we got talking. A couple of weeks ago she mentioned she was going to Europe and her housekeeper hated to stay alone and would I like to live here for a while. Well, I thought, this is *per*fect."

"Exactly," agreed Jupe. "Then you could work fewer hours at the salon, have more time to pursue your acting career, and have a secure place to live."

The girl gave Jupiter an appreciative glance. He seemed to have read her mind.

"Larry Evans said you were worried," she said.

"Larry Evans? The security guard?"

"Yes." She spoke cautiously, as if she was anxious not to give away anything else before she made certain who Jupe was and how much he knew.

Jupe had armed himself with the photograph of Lucille taken when she was runner-up in the Miss Teen Fresno contest. He took it out and put it on the table in front of the girl.

For a moment she said nothing. Then she turned and looked out the window.

"Lucille," said Jupiter, "I got that –"

"Why do you keep calling me that name?" she interrupted angrily. "I'm Arianne! Arianne Ardis!"

"That sounds like a stage name to me," said Jupe.

"What business is it of yours, anyway?" demanded the girl. "Who are you?"

"Your mother and father came to see me and my friends," said Jupe. He told Lucille about tracing the lost tote bag to Fresno. "Your parents drove all night to come and see us. Your mother was crying."

"I *told* them I was okay!" exclaimed the girl.

Jupe felt a moment of relief. She was admitting it! For the first time she was admitting that she was indeed Lucille Anderson.

"Perhaps if you kept in touch with your parents, they'd believe you were safe and well," said Jupe.

"They'd just bug me to go home!" complained Lucille.

"Maybe, but as it stands now, they're imagining that all sorts of horrible things are happening to you. If you were to call them . . ."

"Oh, all right!"

She got up so quickly that she splashed her tea. There was a wall telephone near the sink. She went to it and punched the buttons rapidly.

Jupe sat back, his job finished.

"Hello!" said Lucille after a long moment. "Hello, Mum . . .? Yes, Mum, I really am. Yes. And this kid is here – the chubby kid, you know – and . . ."

There was a pause, then, "Oh good grief, Mum, I don't want to! I'm *fine!* This kid said you just . . ."

There was more from the other end, then suddenly Lucille went rigid with anger. "Didn't you hear me? I won't!" she cried. "I'm fine, and I have a job and a fantastic place to live. I'm going to take some classes and . . ."

Another pause. Then she said sarcastically, "Acting

38

classes, Mum. What did you think? I don't need more algebra!"

Sputtering noises came from the telephone.

"What do you mean Dad's life will never be the same? Don't lay that guilt trip on me," snapped Lucille. "I knew it would be a hassle to call you."

She slammed the telephone down. "I should have known better!" she cried. "Why do I listen to every birdbrain who walks by? Home and mother! You know what that means? One more suffocating year of high school, then marriage to some boring nerd!"

For once Jupiter Jones could not think of a single thing to say.

7

Dracula Lives Again

The Andersons arrived in Rocky Beach that evening before dark. Jupiter, Pete, and Bob were doing some chores for Aunt Mathilda in the salvage yard when the car from Fresno rolled through the gates. Jupiter had called the Andersons as soon as he got back to Headquarters. He had given them Lucille's new name and address and a full account of his talk with her that morning. So why were they here now?

"Oh no!" Pete groaned. "I'm not sure I want to hang around for this one."

The car stopped near the office and Mrs Anderson got out. "You found her!" she cried. She was smiling in spite of the fact that her eyes were red.

"Yes, ma'am," said Jupe. "As I told you on the phone, we found her."

Mrs Anderson looked at Pete. There was a purple lump on his jaw. "I hope that bruise has nothing to do with our daughter," said Mr Anderson. "She hasn't got mixed up with any rough characters, has she?"

"No, ma'am," said Pete.

Mr Anderson came from the car. "I'll be glad when she's safe at home where she belongs." He looked terribly weary.

"I'm surprised that you aren't at Cheshire Square now," remarked Jupe. "Has something gone wrong?"

"Well, you know," began Mrs Anderson, smiling too brightly, "we were wondering if you boys would come too. Lucille might get a bit annoyed, and you seem like such nice boys, and if you're there she won't say some of the things she might if . . ."

Jupiter suddenly realized that the Andersons were afraid of their own daughter. He wished he had never met them.

Pete tried to wander away and get lost. Bob began tinkering intently with a piece of machinery. But in the end the three boys got into the Andersons' car and they all drove to Cheshire Square.

Larry Evans was not at the gate when they arrived. A different guard was on duty. He was delighted to learn that the parents of the girl in the Fowler house had come to see their daughter.

"Maybe you can do something!" he told them, and he waved the car through the gate.

"How swanky!" observed Mrs Anderson, peering back at the gateman.

"What in the name . . ." began Mr Anderson. He was staring across the little park at the house where at least a dozen cars were parked. They were old cars, most of them. Some were stripped down, and some had gleaming chrome tailpipes and garish paint jobs.

Besides the cars, which looked weirdly out of place in the Victorian primness of Cheshire Square, there were the teenagers. Bright floodlights lit a scene that looked as if it belonged in *Animal House*. Kids were everywhere. One boy had climbed to the roof of the Fowler house. He sat leaning against one of the chimneys, scattering popcorn to some pigeons. There were boys on top of the summer house, too. They were cheering on the kids who had decided to hold a breakdancing contest in the driveway.

Over it all was the beat of the music. It was a pounding, thumping, wailing noise that seemed to make the ground vibrate.

"She must be having a party," observed Mrs Anderson.

"That's no party," said Mr Anderson. "That's a riot!"

He had to park four houses down from the Fowler place. As he and Mrs Anderson walked back they saw that the garden was packed with young people. So was the terrace at the side of the house. The Investigators recognized some of the kids from the Pizza Shack.

Most of the crowd were dancing to the blaring music while singing, shouting, and eating pizza that dripped off aqua paper plates. Some wore jewellery made of brilliant neon tubing. A boy dressed mostly in safety pins sported a live snake around his neck. One boy did not dance at all. He was too busy emptying an aquarium into the swimming pool at the edge of the terrace.

Mrs Anderson went up the front steps and rang the doorbell, and the music blared on.

A boy came around the side of the house carrying a box of washing powder. He saw the Andersons and shouted, "Hey, baby! You got company!"

Then he poured the whole box of detergent into the little fountain that bubbled in the front yard.

The music raged on.

The fountain foamed, and then suds poured over the sides and ran down into the grass. The wind picked up masses of soap bubbles and swept them through the air. Soon white sudsy blobs were decorating the nearby hedges and tree limbs.

"Unreal," the boy said admiringly.

Mr Anderson doubled his fists and pounded on the door – and pounded and pounded and pounded.

At last the door opened. A strange creature with dead-white make-up and almost-black lipstick looked out.

"Lucille!" cried Mrs Anderson.

"Who are you this time?" shouted Mr Anderson. "Morticia Addams?"

Lucille tried to slam the door but her father stuck his foot out and stopped her.

"Honey, it's us!" said Mrs Anderson. She held out her arms.

Lucille wavered for a moment, then collapsed, tears flowing, and let herself be embraced. Mrs Anderson's white blouse was quickly smudged with Lucille's dripping black mascara, but Mrs Anderson did not notice.

Mr Anderson said, "Thank heavens!" and leaned against the door. For a minute he just waited while his wife hugged his daughter and his daughter cried. Then he worked his way past them into the house, found the stereo, and shut it off.

The silence was stunning.

The party died quickly after that. The dancers realized that there were parents in their midst and they slipped away.

In minutes Lucille and her mother and father were left with congealing pizzas and drifts of crisps. The Three Investigators, who stood back out of the way, wished they were elsewhere.

When Lucille saw that her party had evaporated, she stopped crying and began to have a minor tantrum. "You ruined it – just like you've ruined my entire life!" she wailed. "You ruined my party that Craig is giving me to celebrate the contract and –"

"Contract?" cried Mr Anderson. "What contract?"

"For *Dracula, Mon Amour*," boasted Lucille. "Oh, Mum! Dad! It's going to be the greatest! And I know you've been worried about me and all, but you can see I'm okay. And I'm learning lots and saving some money, but the best part is the picture. I'm going to be the vampire princess!"

The tears were gone now. Lucille sparkled with her news. "So I'm really getting somewhere, you know, and it's great that I've got a mum and dad who worry about me, but I'm okay. And that's Mr. McLain! Craig! Craig McLain! Come and meet my parents!" she called. "The minute he saw me he knew I'd be perfect for the vampire princess!"

Obviously Mr McLain was the man coming down the stairs. "Good evening," he said. He smiled quickly.

Mrs Anderson stared and Mr Anderson made a growling noise.

Mr McLain was about thirty years old and very smooth. His face was smooth and so was his sandy hair. The carefully styled hair was worn long so that it covered his ears. His tan slacks were a smooth gabardine and his jacket looked silky and wrinkle free.

"Arianne's mother!" he said. His voice was as slick as the rest of him. "I'd have known you anywhere."

It was not an original thing to say, but it seemed to please Mrs Anderson. She was even more pleased when McLain took her hand and held it as if it were a treasure. "I'm so glad you've come," he said. "I felt that I should meet you, even though it will take time to finalize Arianne's contract."

Mrs Anderson made murmuring sounds.

Mr Anderson looked as if he smelled something going rotten in the bottom of a refrigerator. "*Dracula?*" he said. "*Dracula, Mon Amour?*"

"A sequel to the classic Dracula film," oozed Mr McLain. "We wanted an actress – an unknown – to play the role of Mina. I have always felt that Mina Harker would never have settled down to an ordinary life with her dull husband after having known the embrace of the vampire. She would have longed to be with her undead lover again, and in our film she finds a way."

"A neat trick!" snapped Mr Anderson. "If I remember correctly, Dracula turned to dust at the end of the first picture."

"Vampires are not governed by mortal rules," McLain answered, unperturbed. "In our picture Mina finds the secret of restoring the vampire to life and the two are reunited as is their destiny."

Mr Anderson made a choking sound, and just then someone fell down the stairs.

"Ah!" purred Mr McLain. "Allow me to introduce my associate, Henry Morell. He adores dramatic entrances. Henry, do come and meet Arianne's parents."

Henry Morell turned out to be a round-faced, rather chunky individual. He was about as old as McLain, but he was rumpled where McLain was smooth. His short, wet-looking hair was dark and curly and his ears stuck out. He had round dark eyes and a nose that was too small for his face. He grinned foolishly as he scrambled up from the floor at the bottom of the stairs.

"So pleased . . ." Henry mumbled. "Caught my heel . . ."

"Hank has been with Twentieth Century-Fox until recently," said Craig McLain. "Just a few weeks ago he agreed to join us at McLain Productions. He has an incredible background in horror films, and we had a real meeting of the minds. Our film will stimulate our viewers' imaginations rather than deluging them with gore and special effects. The terror will be implied."

"Terrific!" said Mr Anderson sarcastically.

"Lucille, perhaps we had better sit down and have a little talk," Mrs Anderson suggested.

"Not on your life!" Lucille looked as if she was going to have another tantrum. "There's nothing to talk about!"

Mr McLain looked a trifle startled. "*Lucille*, darling? Why, I thought your name was Arianne." When he saw his protégee begin to bristle with anger again, McLain hurried on. "But how dense of me! Arianne is your stage name, of course. Now, dear, I know you'll want some time alone with your parents. All of this must be rather overwhelming at first. I'll be in touch in a day or two. Meanwhile, if you have any questions at all, don't hesitate to call this number."

Mr McLain took a card out of his wallet and handed it to Lucille's father.

"At the moment Hank and I are living a sort of pastoral existence. We're staying at a place up in the hills. It used to belong to Cecil B. DeMille, you know. Would you believe we were awakened this morning by a flock of sheep bleating on the hill behind the house? It's really too much. We don't have a phone yet, but my secretary can always reach me."

Mr Anderson put the card in his pocket without looking at it. "If there is any funny business going on, I will see you in jail," he announced.

"Daddy!" shrieked Lucille.

"I quite understand," cooed Mr McLain. "Any father would feel the same way."

Mr McLain then bowed and poured himself out the door, taking his associate with him.

"And now," said Mr Anderson, "perhaps we can get a few things straight!"

8

A Warning

"Lucille, honey," said Mrs Anderson, "you know that we love you and we trust you."

"To do what?" demanded Mr Anderson.

"If this is your big chance," continued Mrs Anderson, "we want to help you, but –"

"Judy, what are you saying?" cried Mr Anderson.

She turned to him. "We have to trust our own child sooner or later," she said. "She's . . . she's almost grown up. But if it would make you feel better, I can stay here with her."

"Mum, I don't need a babysitter!" cried Lucille. "Anyway, you can't stay here. This isn't your house and it isn't mine either. It's Mrs Fowler's, and I'm taking care of it for her. It's my *job*! Besides, for your information, I also work in a beauty salon!"

"You're a minor," said her father. "If we want you at home, that's where you're going to be."

"Charles, don't!" pleaded Mrs Anderson. "She'll hate you forever."

"Let her," Mr Anderson stated. "She doesn't have to like me. I'm her father."

But Mr Anderson did not sound like a man who was willing to be hated. He grumbled and he threatened a bit longer, but the threats were less and less forceful, and at last he let Mrs Anderson lead him towards the door. At the threshold he stopped and took out his wallet.

"You be careful now, you hear?" he said. He put some money into Lucille's hand, then went on to the car.

No one had bothered to introduce Pete and Bob. All three boys felt awkward to be caught in the midst of this continuing family quarrel. They longed to be back at Headquarters now that Lucille had been found. But it was not to be.

They followed Mr and Mrs Anderson out and got into the car. Mr Anderson suddenly came out with, "Movie producer, my foot! If that sleazeball really is a movie producer, I'll eat my hat!"

The car rolled out of Cheshire Square and down the hill to the main road.

"You may be right, dear," Mrs Anderson said quietly.

"I may?" He sounded astonished.

"Mr McLain looks like a nice young man, but still, we should know more about him."

She turned to the three boys. "If you take his card, can't you check on him?" she implored them. "Aren't there people you can talk to? You were so clever about finding Lucille, surely you can find out whether Mr McLain is really a producer."

Pete groaned to himself.

"I suppose we could find out if he is known in the motion picture industry," said Jupe. "I don't think you have to belong to any union or association to be a producer. I think you just need an idea and some money."

"The guy's a phony!" grumbled Mr Anderson. "Vampire princess! Sounds like an idea he made up right off the top of his head. And that friend of his who fell downstairs – he doesn't seem all there to me."

He turned off the main road and drove through town towards the salvage yard. "Judy, we can compromise," he suggested. "I'll go home and you stay here and keep an eye on things."

She shook her head. "Lucille is determined. We have to give her room to try her wings."

Mr Anderson grumbled some more. He uttered more threats. But when he pulled in at the gate of the salvage yard, he sighed and handed McLain's business card to Jupe.

"Call me in Fresno and let me know what you find out," he said. "If you have to spend some money, do it. I want to get to the bottom of this. I can't believe any sane man would trust Lucille to star in a picture that could cost thousands to make."

"Oh, probably millions!" breathed Mrs Anderson. She sounded really thrilled.

Early the next morning, the Three Investigators were back at Headquarters.

"Our next assignment is to verify that Craig McLain is legitimate," Jupiter said.

"Lucille seems to have a talent for trouble," Bob said. "Do you think the break-in at the Fowler place had anything to do with her?"

"Nah," Pete replied. "People get ripped off all the time. Remember those movie-monster robbers in Hollywood?"

"I tend to agree with Pete," Jupiter said. "Now I suggest calling Hector Sebastian."

Jupiter was referring to the boys' screenwriter friend who had once been a private detective. "He has a lot of contacts in Hollywood," Jupe went on. "He may have heard of Craig McLain."

Don, Mr Sebastian's Vietnamese houseman, answered the telephone. He reported that Mr Sebastian was somewhere in Idaho on location with a company that was shooting a picture. "He will be gone few days, maybe week," said Don. "Not sure. When he comes back I tell him you call."

Jupe thanked Don and hung up, and after a brief conference the boys decided that the most direct method would be the best. "We have Craig McLain's card," said Jupe. "We can go right to his office."

"To question his secretary?" said Bob. "Aren't secretaries paid not to give out any info to strangers?"

"I am sure that just being in the office should enable us to reach some conclusions," said Jupe.

Jupe then placed a call to the Rent-'n'-Ride Auto Rental Company. Thanks to an arrangement made by a grateful client of the boys', they had the occasional use of the agency's antique Rolls-Royce. With it came the services of Worthington, a British chauffeur. Worthington always wore a uniform and treated the Investigators as if they were millionaires, not just a trio of enthusiastic boys. He had become an active ally of the boys, and now considered himself an unofficial partner in the detective firm.

On this morning Worthington and the Rolls were both free, and the gleaming black car with gold-plated trim soon rolled up to the gates of the salvage yard.

When Aunt Mathilda saw the Rolls she groaned. "There's that fancy car again. Now I suppose you'll be busy all day. What about that job I had planned for you, Jupiter?"

"Tomorrow. I promise," swore Jupe. "We've just got to help the Andersons today."

"You always have a good excuse," grumbled Mrs Jones.

The boys set off, bound for the Sunset Strip address on McLain's business card. The drive took almost half an hour. When they reached the Strip, Worthington cruised slowly until he located the address that Jupe had given him.

"There is a parking space at the kerb," he said. "Shall I take it? The Rolls usually attracts attention. Would you prefer to be inconspicuous?"

"I'd prefer to be invisible!" said Bob. "If Lucille Anderson finds out we're checking up on her favourite producer she might throw a tantrum."

"I would not wish to see that happen," said Worthington with a smile. He drove on to a side street and found a parking space there.

"Do we all gang up on McLain?" asked Pete.

Jupe thought a moment. "There's nothing to be gained by outnumbering him," he said. "I'll go in alone."

He got out of the car and trudged back to Sunset.

McLain's office was in a two-storey stucco building that had a coffee shop on the ground floor. The building was not imposing. Jupe went up the stairs and found that McLain Productions Ltd shared the first floor with an accounting firm.

As Jupe put his hand on the doorknob he heard someone say, "Blasted idiot!"

A woman said, "They're holding up production until we get a stunt man there. Hickock won't do the jump himself."

"Okay, get on it," said the first voice. It was not McLain. It was another man who was not nearly so smooth. "We wouldn't have all this trouble if he'd shoot the thing here. How different can a Mexican hill look from one in Griffith Park?"

Jupiter turned the knob and opened the door.

He saw a woman with curly grey hair and rimless glasses. She was at a desk and had a telephone in her hand.

A balding man with fierce blue eyes scowled at Jupe, then strode away into an inner office and slammed the door behind him.

"Can I help you?" said the woman. She did not put down the telephone.

"Is Mr McLain here?" asked Jupe.

"This isn't a good time," said the woman. "Why do you want to see Mr McLain?"

"I – I met him yesterday evening," said Jupe, who had had a sudden inspiration. "We were at the home of a mutual friend. It occurred to me that he might be able to use me in his production."

"Use you?"

"I've had some experience," said Jupe. "If there is a part for a juvenile in the Dracula picture . . ."

"Mr McLain!" the woman shouted.

The balding man opened his door and looked out.

"Mr McLain, this kid says he met you last night at somebody's house. He's talking about some kind of Dracula picture."

The man came out of his office. "Dracula? I don't have enough trouble with a company shooting in Ensenada? I need somebody asking me about Dracula?"

Jupe stared at him for a second or two, then took out the business card that Lucille's father had given him. Without a word he handed it to the bald man.

The man looked at the card and he snorted.

"The man who gave me that card last night said I could reach him here," said Jupe. "He said his name was Craig McLain. It appears he was not telling the truth."

"You can bet your boots he wasn't telling the truth,"

said the bald man. "Did the guy say he'd give you a job in pictures?"

"Actually, it was a girl who was going to get the job," Jupe went on. Then, very briefly, he recounted the tale of Lucille Anderson.

"And he's giving out my business cards," said the bald Mr McLain. "Sorry, kid, but I am not about to make a Dracula picture. It isn't what I do. I do documentaries and some commercials. I don't have any parts for a juvenile right now, and I'd advise that girl who thinks she'll be in a Dracula film to think again. Tell her to forget it and land herself a nice job waiting tables. Does she have any money?"

Jupiter shook his head. "No. She doesn't."

"She a friend of yours?"

"I've known her for a brief time."

"Tell her to be careful about men who claim to be film producers – especially if they use someone else's business cards."

"I will," said Jupiter. "Do you have any idea who the man might really be? Has this happened to you before?"

The bald man shrugged. "Not to me. But I give out plenty of business cards because that's what they're for. You give them to people and say, 'Call me sometime. I may have a part for you.' Sometimes they call and sometimes they don't. What did the guy look like?"

"About thirty," said Jupe. "Light brown hair. Very smooth. He said he was staying in the hills in a place that used to belong to Cecil B. DeMille."

"That's safe," said McLain. "DeMille's dead!"

Then he looked thoughtful. "If you're a friend of that girl's, tell her to back off right away. Sometimes these guys who act like big shots are after money, and that's bad enough. But if they're weirdos, they can be really dangerous!"

9

Fade-out into Fear

Larry Evans was on duty at Cheshire Square when the Rolls-Royce came up the hill. He stepped out of his gatehouse to stare.

"I'm impressed!" he exclaimed. "Boy, am I impressed! Does Arianne know about this? Or will it be a big surprise?"

"It'll be a surprise all right," said Pete. "When she hears what we've got to say, she'll be very surprised."

"Is she at home?" Jupe asked.

"Yep!" said the guard. "That guy with the long hair and the snooty attitude was here with his pal earlier, but they left a while ago. I'll call her."

He stepped back into his little house. Through the window the boys could see him push some buttons on the telephone, then wait and wait. At last he frowned and put the phone down.

"No answer at the Fowler house," he said.

"Maybe she went out somewhere?" Bob suggested.

Larry Evans shook his head. "I'd have seen her."

Jupe felt a sudden dread. "She wasn't with McLain when he left, was she?"

"No," the guard told them. "McLain's sidekick was with him – that fat little guy with the curly hair. But not Arianne."

Now the security man looked worried. It was plain that he had orders to admit no one to Cheshire Square without clearing them with a resident. "Let me try again," he said. He went back to the phone, pushed the buttons again, and waited some more. When he got no answer he waved the Rolls through the gate.

"Bang on the door," he directed. "Check the swimming pool. If you don't find her, come back and get me."

Worthington drove in and circled the little park. The

Fowler house was quiet now, but there was still debris left from the party the night before. A paper plate had been shoved in under the shrubbery. When the Three Investigators went up the walk, popcorn crackled under their feet.

Jupe rang the doorbell. Chimes sounded inside the house, but no one came to the door.

"She isn't here," said Bob.

"Something's wrong," said Jupe. "I'm sure something's wrong."

"I'll go back to the gate," said Pete. "The guard must have a master key."

He rushed off, passing the Rolls where Worthington waited. While he was gone, Jupiter and Bob circled the house. They saw no sign of Lucille.

The guard was waiting with Pete when Jupe and Bob got back to the front porch. Worthington was there too, looking anxious. The security man opened the front door with his master key. They all went into the hall, where bits and pieces of Lucille's party were still scattered around.

"Lucille!" called Jupiter.

No one answered.

The boys began a quick search. It took no time at all to go through the lower floor. When they went upstairs, Larry Evans went with them. Worthington stayed in the lower hall to keep watch.

There were closed doors uptstairs, which Evans opened one after another. The boys looked into darkened, unused bedrooms where the drapes were drawn. At the end of the hall was a room that was obviously very much in use. There was a wide bed, with its pastel pink covers thrown back. A pair of slippers with white fur rabbit heads on the toes were tossed under a chair. A quilted satin robe was thrown across the foot of the bed.

Larry Evans opened a curtain and sunlight flooded into the room.

"This must be where Lucille sleeps," said Jupe.

"I think it's Mrs Fowler's room, when Mrs Fowler is at home," said Evans. He glanced at the dressing table where there were crystal perfume bottles on a little tray.

"Arianne's a nice kid, but she shouldn't be using this room and Mrs Fowler's things."

Pete began to prowl about. He opened a door in an alcove and saw a closet that was as large as most people's bedrooms. It was jammed with clothes.

"Didn't Mrs Fowler go to Europe?" asked Pete. "What did she take with her if she left all this stuff behind?"

No one even tried to answer that one. Jupe was pulling at his lower lip, scowling at the carpeting. It was a sign that his mental machinery was in high gear. "Isn't there another gate?" he said to Evans. "Couldn't she have gone out that way without passing you?"

"There's a back entrance, sure," said Evans. "It's for dustbin lorries and deliveries and repairmen. But it's always locked."

"Who keeps the key?" said Jupe.

"There is no key. When somebody has to use that gate, they let me know. I open the gate with a switch in my gatehouse."

"Maybe Lucille's just gone to visit a neighbour," suggested Bob.

"Not likely," replied Larry Evans. "Arianne doesn't mix much with the other residents."

Pete opened another door. He expected to see another closet. Instead the door led into a bathroom where bubble bath flowed over the top of a filled marble bath. The air was thick with a floral scent. A marble counter with two sinks held more jars and bottles. One bottle had overturned, and an amber stain had spread over the marble and then dribbled down to the floor.

"Messy kid," said Bob.

"Perhaps not quite that messy," Jupe decided. He was at the bathroom door looking in at the disorder. "Suppose she was in the bath when the telephone rang. She learned that McLain was at the gate and she gave word to let him in. Then she threw on some clothes and went down to open the door – and something happened. It was something so violent, or so important, that she never got back to empty the bath."

"I vote for the violent bit," said Bob. "Somebody chased her up here and the perfume got spilled when she struggled with the guy."

"You kids are making too much of this," said Evans. The guard looked very nervous. "Look, she's a sloppy kid and she just doesn't automatically empty the bath unless somebody nags. She's used to having a mother pick up after her. She spills perfume and she figures she'll clean it up when she gets around to it. She goes down and lets McLain in and . . . and . . ."

"And what?" said Jupe. "Where is she? If she didn't go away with McLain and she doesn't visit the neighbours, what happened to her?"

It was Bob who found the little guest towel. He was near the dressing table, and the wastebasket was almost at his feet when he looked down.

"Hey, look at this!" He bent and fished the towel out. It was white, with a butterfly embroidered near one end. It was stained a rusty red.

"Is this what I'm afraid it is?" said Bob.

Larry Evans looked and winced. "Blood," he said. He reached to touch the towel. "It's still damp. You're right. Something happened here this morning. I'm calling the police!"

10

The Lady Vanishes

Chief Reynolds came in person. He looked at the chaos in the bathroom and his expression was grim.

He scowled at Larry Evans. "You said she had a visitor this morning? Did you get the number of his licence plate?"

"Yes, Chief," replied Evans. "It's on the log in the gate-house. But I could swear the girl didn't leave in that car."

"She left somehow," said the chief, and he went downstairs.

"I'll talk to neighbours," the chief added. "Somebody might have seen something. You boys, go on home. I don't want you messing around here, you understand?"

"Chief Reynolds –" Jupe began.

"Get going!" said the chief. "This is now police business!"

Worthington drove the trio of young detectives back to the salvage yard. At first a gloomy silence reigned in the car.

Then Pete spoke up. "Well, this case beats everything."

"What do you mean?" asked Bob.

"We find a tote bag on the beach," Pete went on, "and try to locate the owner. Seems simple – just call the library. Instead we find out the owner is lost as well as the bag. So we find her. But her parents want us to keep going. This time we're supposed to find the guy who gives the girl a job. Except he gets lost too . . . or maybe he never existed. When we try to warn the girl about him, she disappears on us again."

"And just when the case begins to be interesting," Jupe added, "the police refuse to allow us to remain involved."

"This case is going to drive us nuts!" concluded Pete.

Worthington dropped off the boys and drove away. Jupiter stared at the gates of the yard. They were closed. This was almost unheard of in the middle of the day.

"Where are Uncle Titus and Aunt Mathilda?" Jupe wondered out loud.

"I can guess," said Bob. "They've heard that some old building in Nome, Alaska, is being wrecked, and they've gone to see if they can latch on to the rusty water pipes or the chipped sink."

The explanation was offered in jest, but it turned out to be not too far off the mark. Konrad appeared from inside the yard and told Jupiter that his uncle was in Los Angeles collecting salvage from a demolished building there.

"Your aunt, she is across the street cooking something," said Konrad. "I am keeping the gate locked because I am busy and there is too much stuff here that somebody can pick up and carry away."

Konrad went to the office for the key. When he unlocked the big gates he said, "If you stay here and serve the customers, I won't have to lock up again."

Jupe agreed that he would stay near the gates, and Pete and Bob left for their homes. For a while Jupe just sat on the steps of the office and brooded about Lucille Anderson. In his mind's eye he saw again the disorder in the bathroom. What had happened? The guard had not seen the girl leave Cheshire Square. Had she been in the boot of McLain's car? Or had she just run away again? But what was the meaning of the red-stained towel?

After a time another thought came to make Jupe uneasy. Where was Aunt Mathilda? Why had she been gone so long? She did sometimes leave the yard to put something on the stove to simmer, but she was never gone for more than a few minutes.

"Konrad?" Jupe shouted.

Konrad came, looking sweaty.

"I'm going to the house for a minute," said Jupe. "I want to check on something."

"Okay!" said Konrad. "I watch the gate."

Jupe went across the street to the Jones house and found the kitchen door ajar.

There was no one in the kitchen. There was nothing on the stove. An empty pot lay on the floor where someone had dropped it. The lid had come off and rolled into a corner.

Suddenly Jupe felt cold.

He listened. The house was absolutely silent. Should he call? Was Aunt Mathilda here? Or was there someone else in the house – someone who had startled Aunt Mathilda and made her drop the pot and . . . and what? Where was she?

He went to the dining room door. He looked in at a confusion of dishes and linens strewn across the floor. Drawers were pulled out of the sideboard. Cutlery was scattered over the linens.

Jupe's mouth was dry. He wanted to call out, but decided not to. The intruder might still be there – and he might have Aunt Mathilda with him!

Jupe picked his way through the dining room. In the living room knickknacks and books were scattered around. Drawers had been pulled out of the lamp tables and dumped on the floor. Beyond the living rooms was the front hall where a wardrobe was open. Coats and jackets and boots had been hauled out and then dropped.

Still no sign of Aunt Mathilda!

Uncle Titus' den had also been ransacked, and the tape deck and turntable were gone. So was the amplifier. The stereo speakers still remained. The thief might have found them too clumsy for him to drag away. Or had he been disturbed before he could take them?

Disturbed! That was it! Aunt Mathilda had come in from the salvage yard. She had put down the cashbox she carried with her in the yard, and the thief had heard her.

At that instant Jupe remembered seeing the cashbox. When he came through the kitchen it had been there on the counter next to the small television set.

Jupe went quickly back to the kitchen. The box was still there. He opened it and saw that there was money inside. A lot of money. Aunt Mathilda had had nearly a hundred dollars when she came into the kitchen. And the burglar had left it untouched.

Why? Where was she?

"Aunt Mathilda?" he called. His voice was unsteady.

Then he heard it. "Hrwrowf! Hrruff muh! Trsss!" The muffled cries were followed by thumps and rattles.

Jupiter flew to the little service porch that opened off the kitchen. It was where the washer and drier were kept. A broom cupboard was in one corner. The noise came from there.

The cupboard door was jammed shut. A broom had been wedged tightly between it and the washing machine, with the handle against the door and the business end of the broom against the washer.

"Aunt Mathilda!" cried Jupe. "Are you all right? It's me, Jupiter!"

More furious sounds came from the cupboard and Jupe yanked at the broom. It came away in his hands and the cupboard door popped open.

Aunt Mathilda tumbled out onto the service porch. Dust cloths and cans of cleanser exploded out along with her.

"Jupiter! At last!"

Her face was very red. Her hair stood on end. She sat on the floor and glared.

"Just let me get my hands on that wretch!" Aunt Mathilda swore. "He'll wish he'd never been born!"

11

Jupe Pleads for Help

The police arrived in a few minutes. By then Aunt Mathilda was seated at the kitchen table scowling into a cup of coffee Jupe had made her.

"Are you able to tell us what happened, ma'am?" one of the officers asked her.

Aunt Mathilda certainly could, and she told it with a great deal of passion. She had come into the house planning to set some soup bones to simmering. She had just taken the stock pot from the cupboard when she heard something move in the dining room. Thinking that it might be Jupiter, she had called out.

A moment later someone had seized her from behind and pressed something soft and suffocating over her face. The stock pot had dropped to the floor in the struggle. Then she had been shoved and wrestled to the broom cupboard and shut in there. She had not even glimpsed the intruder; he had been behind her the whole time. She did have the impression that there was only one assailant.

The officer who was making out the report found a scatter cushion in the bottom of the broom cupboard. "This is probably what the guy used," he decided. "Do you think he stayed in the house for long after he shut you in the cupboard? Or do you think he left right away? He didn't touch the cashbox and he left the silverware behind, as if he panicked."

"Panic! I'd like to make him panic!" declared Aunt Mathilda. "I'm not sure, but I don't think he stayed long. I couldn't hear him for quite a while before Jupiter came in. And when Jupiter did come, I thought it might be the thief moving around in the kitchen, so I kept quiet."

The officer and his partner went through the house and found that a screen was off one of the dining room windows. "He most likely came in that way," said one of the police officers to Jupe. "Your aunt must have come in before he had a chance to haul all his loot out of here, and even though he did shut her in the cupboard, he must have been too rattled to finish his job. Burglary's a nervous business, I guess. Guys who break into places can get spooked and beat it, even when there's no reason."

The police eventually went off, warning Aunt Mathilda that there was little hope of recovering the missing stereo equipment. By the time they drove away Uncle Titus was home and Jupiter had tidied up most of the mess. Konrad was fixing the screen. Jupe headed back to his workshop in the corner of the salvage yard.

Pete was there when Jupe came in. He was sitting on the workbench tinkering with his bike.

"I saw the cops down the street," he said. "Were they at your house? I'd have gone and watched like everybody else on the block, but the cops just tell you that you'll see it on the six o'clock news. And then you never do."

"You won't see this, certainly," said Jupe, and he quickly recounted the story of Aunt Mathilda and the burglar. "Rocky Beach is getting more than its share of trouble. Lucille was burgled two days ago and today Aunt Mathilda was too."

Pete asked, "Are we going to look for Aunt Mathilda's burglar? Or are we going to leave this one to the cops?"

"Leave it to the police, I suppose," said Jupiter. "It seems to be just another routine break-in."

"So that just leaves us with the case of Lucille Anderson," said Pete.

Jupe looked a bit doubtful. "Not if Chief Reynolds has his way. Remember he told us to stay out of it from this point on." Then he brightened. "But we still have the responsibility of calling the Andersons and telling them what we've learned so far."

"What do you mean 'we'?" retorted Pete. "I'll leave that job to *you*. It's not that I don't like the Andersons, it's just that they remind me of my mum's favourite soap opera, *Family in Furore*."

Jupe grimaced, but he pulled aside the grating that

concealed Tunnel Two. With Pete behind him, he crawled the distance to the trailer. Once the boys were inside, Jupe dialled the Andersons' house in Fresno. He listened to the telephone at the other end ring and ring. When he counted ten rings, he hung up. "Not home," he said.

"Chief Reynolds may have called them already," said Pete. "They may be on their way here."

"Quite possible," said Jupe. "Now, what leads do we have? McLain's business card turned out to be bogus. And his partner who . . . who . . ."

Jupe was suddenly silent, his hand still on the telephone.

"Who what?" demanded Pete. "You've thought of something."

"Henry Morell," said Jupe. "The man who calls himself McLain said Morell had been at Twentieth Century-Fox until recently. Wouldn't it be funny if he were telling the truth?"

Pete was already pulling the telephone book off the bottom shelf of the bookcase. He located the number of the film studio and read it to Jupe, who dialled.

Jupe began by asking to speak to Henry Morell. The operator sounded totally indifferent and announced that she did not have that name in her directory. Jupe then asked to speak to someone in personnel. When he was connected he said he was a cousin of Henry Morell's, visiting Los Angeles unexpectedly, and that he was trying to contact Morell.

"You always have to make a five-act opera out of everything," muttered Pete.

Jupe put his hand over the mouthpiece. "What should I say? That I'm an employer looking for a reference? I don't think they'd believe me."

But then the woman in the personnel office at Twentieth Century-Fox was back on the line, reporting that she had no record of a Henry Morell.

Jupe thanked her and hung up.

"So much for that," he said. "Not a trace. Nowhere to start. A couple of people who came out of nowhere, latched on to Lucille Anderson, then vanished."

"How about the Pizza Shack?" said Pete. "Maybe the kids there know something. They were at Lucille's party, and they may have noticed something about McLain and his buddy. Maybe somebody even knows them."

It was a slim chance, but it was a chance nonetheless. Jupe and Pete went back out through Tunnel Two and Jupe got his bike. They didn't call Bob to ask him to join them since he was working at the library that afternoon. Jupe and Pete swooped down into town to the main road, and across to the Pizza Shack.

The music was pounding, as usual, and the video games were blinking and beeping. Kids were clustered around small tables where they ate and talked.

One of the boys who had been at the Fowler House recognized Pete and Jupiter when they came in.

"Hey!" he yelled. He grinned and beckoned to the boys to join him. "The kid brothers! How's it going?"

"Not well," Jupiter told him. "And we are not anyone's kid brothers. We're friends of Lucille's, and we're looking for her."

"Not brothers?" said the older boy. "You could have fooled me. When Arianne, or Lucille, or whatever her name is, ignored you I thought you must be her kid brothers or something. That's what my sister always does to me."

He moved over to make room for Jupe to sit beside him. Pete took a place across the table.

"Lucille Anderson has disappeared from Cheshire Square," Jupe told him. "We think she may have been kidnapped."

The older boy gasped. "You're putting me on," he said.

Jupe shook his head. "She was at the Fowler house this morning. She talked to the guard. And then the man who calls himself McLain came to see her, along with Henry Morell, and no one has seen her since."

The other boy was motionless for a second, then yelled, "Hey, you guys, come over here a second. Listen to the story this kid's giving me."

The video machines stopped making blips and bleeps, and people drifted near to listen to Jupe's tale. The plump woman behind the counter leaned forward as well.

Jupe told of Lucille's disappearance, neglecting none of the details. He mentioned the bath filled with bubble bath, the spilled perfume, and the red-stained towel in the waste-basket. "There may have been a struggle," he said, "and McLain and Morell may have taken her away. Some of you have met McLain. That isn't his real name, incidentally. We don't know what his real name is, and at the moment it doesn't seem likely that we'll find out in a hurry. Not unless someone here has some information."

It was silent in the Pizza Shack.

The door opened and the grey-haired man who seemed to be in charge of the place came in. He saw the group around Jupiter and Pete.

"What's going on?" he said, looking at the waitress.

"These boys are looking for their friend, Mr Sears," said the woman. "Such a pretty girl. She came in here a lot and played the video games, and now she's missing. They think somebody took her away."

"Kidnapped?" said the man. His eyebrows shot up.

"It looks like it," replied the woman.

Jupe turned to the woman behind the counter. "Do you remember anything about the man who gave that party last night? He served lots of pizza. Did he get it here?"

She nodded. "A slick one, he is," she said. "I thought at the time, Why is he hanging around with that mixed-up kid? He's too old for her and her friends."

"He's a big Hollywood producer," said the boy next to Jupe, "or so he said. I don't know. That's suppposed to be just a line, isn't it? 'You're great, baby, and I'll put you in pictures.' Except when that guy walked in here yesterday and spotted Arianne . . ."

"They met here?" Jupe asked quickly.

"Yeah. She was playing the video games, and when he came in with that creepy little guy, you could see them kind of do a take on Arianne. They talked to each other for a second, and watched her, and then McLain goes up and introduces himself. He acts like he just stumbled over a big gold nugget or something. And he says she is just what he is looking for."

One of the girls who had been at the party came drifting over to the table and sat down. "Arianne is not too firmly plugged into reality, if you know what I mean," she told Jupe. "She really does believe that being able to twirl a baton will get her into movies, and when the guy says he's a producer and he wants to give her a part in a picture, she lights up like a Christmas tree. The next thing you know she's sitting with those guys while they have a pizza. And then they invite everybody in the place to a party to celebrate Arianne's new job."

"I don't get it," said Pete. "Why would he want to invite everybody to a party?"

"He didn't want her to think he was some kind of a weirdo, and he thought she'd be more comfortable with her friends around," said the girl. "At least that's what he said."

The girl looked serious. "It did seem like he had to be okay when he wanted us all there. I mean, we always get told not to go places alone with strangers, and not to get into cars or anything, and that there's safety in numbers. Last night was really a trip! There must have been fifty people there. So . . . so she really is missing, is she?"

Jupe nodded.

The girl looked worried. "I tried calling her at the Tender Touch," she said. "That's where she works. Only she didn't go in today and they were cross. I wanted to know what happened with her parents."

"Her parents went home to Fresno," said Jupiter. "Only by now they may be back here, if Chief Reynolds reached them."

"Why do you say that guy's name isn't McLain?" asked one of the boys in the crowd. "Are you sure?"

"We met the real Craig McLain this morning," said Jupe. "He is definitely not the man who was at the party."

"Craig?" said the boy. "He said his name was Craig McLain? His friend called him something else – something really weird."

"Iggy," said one of the girls. "That's what he called him."

"Iggy?" It was the man behind the counter speaking now.

Everyone looked at him, and he was suddenly flustered. "What kind of a name is Iggy?" he said. He shook his head. "A bad person, running off with a young girl! It's a cruel time we live in."

No one was inclined to disagree with him. Jupe and Pete waited to see if anyone could recall any more details about the bogus film producer. No one could.

The man was as shadowy as smoke!

12

Attacked!

The Andersons arrived in Rocky Beach sometime during the night. They appeared at the Jones house shortly after 8:00 A.M., looking haggard and red-eyed. They had already been to see Chief Reynolds.

Aunt Mathilda had completely recovered from her frightening ordeal of the day before, and she bustled about doing what she could for the distraught couple from Fresno. Aid and comfort from Aunt Mathilda usually took the form of food, but that day she could not tempt the Andersons to eat anything.

"I can't believe nobody saw anything," said Mr Anderson. "None of the neighbours. The chief talked to them, and not one saw Lucille leave the house with those two creeps. And the car McLain was driving turns out to be registered to somebody named Henry Vance. Vance sold it to somebody named Smith a while back and Smith didn't register it again, so the licence number wasn't a help. The car is grey and that's all we know. We called the place where Lucille works. It's a beauty salon. The old bat who answered the phone didn't even try to be helpful."

He sounded really bitter.

"Mr Anderson, you're tired and your wife looks exhausted," said Aunt Mathilda. "Why don't you rest here for a few hours? We have a spare bedroom. We'll let you know if anything happens."

"No." He looked agitatedly out the window of the Jones living room. "We have a room reserved at the Rocky Beach Inn. It should be ready by now. We'll check in there and wait to hear from Chief Reynolds or . . . or anyone who has something to tell us. A neighbour is covering our telephone at home in case the kidnappers call us there. It might be simple, you know." He looked hopeful. "They might want a ransom."

Mrs Anderson got up as if she were sleepwalking.

"I know you did the best you could," said Mr Anderson to Jupiter. "I want to thank you and your friends."

He went out, leading Mrs Anderson by the arm.

Jupiter went out to his workshop and crawled through Tunnel Two to Headquarters. Pete and Bob were already there.

"Morning," said Pete. He was sitting on the floor, leaning against the filing cabinet and looking sleepy. "I saw the Andersons' car at your house, so I called Bob to come right over. Anything new?"

"No." Jupe took his accustomed place behind the desk. "The Andersons are checking into the Rocky Beach Inn. I expect they'll stay there until there is word."

"Let's hope there *is* word," said Bob. He was going through notes he had jotted down in a small notebook. "Every approach we try seems to end at a blank wall. Those two guys who set up the party for Lucille seem to have come out of nowhere – and disappeared back into it. At least one is using a fake name. Probably the other is too. Remember, no one knew Morell at Twentieth Century-Fox."

Jupe frowned. "A lot of things don't add up. Those two *could* just be a pair of freaks who picked Lucille at random and grabbed her. But they took a great many unnecessary chances if kidnapping was their only motive. They showed themselves to a whole gang of her friends, they gave a party for Lucille, and they met her parents. That's not what you expect from kidnappers."

Jupiter put the fingertips of both hands together, forming a little cage. "And then there is the unexplained intruder – the one who broke into the Fowler house before Lucille met McLain and Morell. Could he have been one of them – either McLain or Morell? If so, why did he break into the house? To get Lucille? Or to take something from the house?"

"Coincidence?" Bob asked. "Like that vampire scare at the pawnshop where Lucille pawned her pin? That seems a coincidence. Robbers wearing scary costumes have held up all kinds of places all over town – places that have nothing to do with Lucille, as far as we know."

Pete sighed. "We could keep chewing this over all day," he said. "It still gets us nowhere. Lucille has disappeared along with a couple of totally unknown guys and, until we find them, we are up the creek."

The little plastic tote bag that the boys had found on the beach was still in the office. The boys had forgotten to bring it to Cheshire Square when they went to see Lucille. Bob took it down from the top of the filing cabinet and dumped it on the desk. He stared at the collection of make-up and the library book and the teddy bear, as if one of these objects might be a clue to Lucille's whereabouts. The bear, made of silky dark brown fur, stared at the boys with its blank button eyes.

Jupiter picked up the library book and thumbed through it. Passages were marked on a number of pages.

" 'Each night, as you wait to sleep, repeat the words "success, love, riches." Picture yourself enjoying these things,' " Jupiter intoned. " 'As surely as the sun rises, success, love, and material wealth will be yours!' "

The Three Investigators looked at each other and chuckled.

Pete grabbed the little teddy bear and addressed it ponderously. "Imagine yourself enjoying the fresh breezes in a lush forest. Who knows, tomorrow you may wake up as Smokey the Bear!"

The boys laughed again, then Pete and Bob left to go home.

Jupe continued to sit in the trailer and he continued to brood. He stared at the furry teddy bear on the desk where Pete had tossed it, and felt that there was a clue somewhere that he was missing. Behind the series of bizarre events there might be a pattern, and if he could find it he might be able to find Lucille.

He put the bear back into the tote bag, then the book, and finally gathered up the cosmetics that were scattered over the desk top.

And suddenly, just outside the trailer, something moved.

He held his breath and listened. What was it? Was some small animal rooting around in the junk that was piled around the trailer?

The faint noise came again, so soft that it could hardly be distinguished from the sound of the breeze. Softer, really, than a breeze. Something sighed, as if a weary being waited just outside – waited for Jupiter.

At that moment Jupe knew he would have to check outside Headquarters. Something – or someone – was out there, and Jupe couldn't breathe easy until he knew what it was.

He got up, careful not to let his chair scrape on the floor. He stepped around the desk, then stopped and listened.

Now there was silence.

It was only an animal, Jupe told himself sternly. A ground squirrel had chosen to take up residence in the salvage outside. Or a stray cat with kittens. Or a rat? A rat would be horrible, but rats were creatures that could be dealt with.

The quickest way out of Headquarters was Easy Three, and Jupiter went out that exit. A door opened from the office directly into a huge discarded iron boiler, big enough to hold Jupiter easily or even an adult. In turn the boiler led on to a short passage through a pile of granite blocks, ending at a large oak door still in its frame. Jupe peeked out through the oak door into the salvage yard and looked around cautiously. Nothing out of the ordinary showed.

The First Investigator scouted around the yard for a few minutes, finding no little animal or mysterious intruder. He then returned to his outside workshop. Puffing, he laboured through Tunnel Two and re-entered Headquarters. He gave a quick glance around the office. The tote bag was on the desk where he had left it.

But he saw that there was a change. A notepad had been open on the desk, close to the telephone. While Jupe had been checking through the salvage outside, someone had slipped into Headquarters and had turned the notepad around to read what was written on it. A chill went up Jupiter's spine.

There was nothing important on the pad. Jupe had used it to doodle on. But he knew that an intruder had been there. And suddenly he knew that the intruder was still there!

Jupe remained motionless, sensing a presence behind him. He had his back to the curtain that separated the office from the small photographic darkroom. Jupe felt that what had crept so silently into Headquarters was just behind that curtain – waiting . . . breathing. . . .

The breathing was so soft at first that he could hardly be sure. But then the sound grew louder. It was horrible – a rough, rasping noise that was almost in Jupe's ear.

Then a demonic laugh filled the room!

Jupe leaped away from the curtain. He spun around to face the intruder.

The curtain was snatched aside. Jupe stared at a hideous being – a thing of scales and jagged teeth, with a face of formless, melting horror.

The thing laughed again. A dark claw reached for Jupe.

Jupe dodged, crashed into the desk, tried to duck sideways.

The laughing horror struck!

Jupe felt the blow, then saw the metal filing cabinet rush to meet him.

His head crashed into the cabinet and everything went dark!

13

Tracking a Bear

"He wanted something in the tote!" said Jupe. "I saw that the tote was missing as soon as I came to, and I realized it then. The tote bag was what the burglar was looking for when he shut Aunt Mathilda in the broom cupboard. It's the reason Lucille was kidnapped. And the monster found it when he got in here!"

Jupiter had called Pete and Bob as soon as he had his wits about him. They had hurried to Headquarters and they now faced Jupe across the desk. He was still white-faced and shaken. And they were shocked too. Someone had got past their carefully constructed defenses. Jupe had been attacked right in their secret stronghold!

"And I made it so easy for him," Jupe added ruefully. "I heard something rustling outside and barged out Easy Three and just showed him the way in! He was waiting for me when I returned!"

Jupe shuddered at the memory of the hideous face and the reaching, claw-like hands.

Pete had his own horrible memory of the masked creature who had charged out of the pawnbroker's shop. "Was it the same mask?" he said now. "The werewolf mask that the guy was wearing the other day?"

"No, but it certainly could be the same man." Jupe was quieter now. Some of the colour had come back into his face. "McLain and Morell were students of horror films. At least they talked as if they were. They might consider it artistic to commit crimes while disguised as characters from creep shows."

"Makes the guy who tried to rob the house in Cheshire Square look real boring," and Bob. "A plain old stocking over the head – just like all the other crooks."

"Except for one thing," said Jupe. "Lucille Anderson was involved. So it could have been the same man."

"Right!" said Pete. "But what did the monster want in the tote? The pawn tickets?"

"The tickets Lucille had slipped into the book?" Jupe frowned. "I don't think so. The things Lucille pawned were so ordinary. They couldn't be worth much. A baby ring, a medal for spelling, and a little gold pin. She received just a few dollars for the lot. No one would go after the tickets. Also, let's not forget that the pawnbroker who had Lucille's pin was only one of several people who were robbed by make-believe monsters. I doubt the pin had anything to do with it."

"I think I have a headache," said Pete miserably. "If it wasn't the pawn tickets that the ghoul wanted, what was it? The book?"

"A library book?" Bob laughed. "No way. Not unless there was something written in it. Lucille could have made notes. But what about? She didn't seem as if she had any guilty secret to hide. She was just trying to avoid her parents long enough to find a part in a movie."

"The teddy bear!" said Jupe suddenly.

Bob and Pete stared at him. "What about the teddy bear?" Pete wanted to know.

"What if that's what the monster was after?" asked Jupe. "It was not an ordinary toy. Most teddy bears are made of plush. That one was real fur."

"So what?" said Pete. "Even if the bear was made out of the rarest mink on earth, it wouldn't be worth that much trouble."

"Suppose there was something inside the bear?" suggested Jupe.

"Now you're talking!" cried Bob. "That has to be it! Jewels. Or drugs. McLain and Morell know Lucille has a toy bear that is loaded with something really valuable. They get into the Fowler house to look for it and she interrupts them. When they come back for it and don't find it, they take her with them to make her tell where it is. She says we must have it, which we do. They search your house, Jupe, still don't find it, and then they follow us here."

"Meanwhile, they keep Lucille with them so she can't call the cops," finished Pete.

"A beautiful theory," said Jupiter. "It fits all the facts as we know them. It even explains why Aunt Mathilda's cashbox was left untouched. And why there was a blood-stained towel in the Fowler bathroom."

"Yes," said Pete. "There was a struggle – and somebody got hurt!"

Jupe was now in high gear. His eyes glinted as he picked up the telephone. "The first thing we must find out is how Lucille got that bear," he announced. "It's the only clue we have to the phantom intruder. It's the only clue we have to Lucille's whereabouts!"

With his free hand Jupe was flipping the pages of the telephone directory. "Here it is," he said. "The Rocky Beach Inn."

He dialled a number and then asked for Mr Anderson. When the man came on the line, Jupe said, "Jupiter Jones here. We may have a clue we can follow up. Remember that teddy bear in Lucille's tote bag? Did she take it with her when she left Fresno? It's a bear that's made out of real fur."

"Teddy bear?" echoed Mr Anderson. "Just a second, I'll ask my wife."

Jupe could hear some muffled conversation. In a few moments Mr Anderson got back on the phone. "Judy doesn't remember a fur bear as one of the toys Lucille had on her bed," he informed Jupe. "As far as we know, Lucille took clothes and make-up with her and that's all. Why?"

"We're not sure, Mr Anderson, but if the bear is something Lucille acquired here, we may have just had the break we need. We'll be in touch with you, and thanks very much."

Jupe hung up. "She got the bear here," he said. "Okay. Where did she get it? And how could we find out about a thing like that?"

"The Pizza Shack?" said Bob. "Maybe some of the kids there know about it."

"It's a place to start," said Jupe.

Minutes later the boys were crossing the Pacific Coast

Highway. When they entered the Piza Shack several of the regular customers recognized them and waved. The woman behind the counter smiled.

"They don't eat much," she said to grey-haired Mr Sears, who was again at the cash register. "But they're nice boys all the same. Always polite."

Mr Sears made no comment, but he watched and he listened as Jupe asked the other kids whether any of them remembered the teddy bear that Arianne Ardis had carried in her tote bag.

"Teddy bear?" said one of the boys. "You're kidding! She carried a teddy bear around with her?"

"Lots of kids do," said a girl with blood-red lipstick and maroon eye shadow. "It's not so weird. Arianne's was real cute. Mink! I asked her where she got it but she wouldn't tell."

"Had she had the bear long when you asked her?" asked Jupe.

The girl shrugged. 'A day or two, I guess."

No one else in the Pizza Shack knew anything about the bear so the Three Investigators thanked everyone and left.

"Okay," said Pete, "so who do we ask now?"

"Toy stores would seem logical," said Jupiter.

Pete groaned. "Do you realize how many stores around here sell teddy bears?"

"Attention to detail is what makes a successful detective," countered Jupiter.

There was a toy shop not a quarter of a mile from the Pizza Shack, and the boys started their search there. Pete groaned again when he saw the throngs of bears in the place. "How will we ever be able to tell where Lucille got her bear?" he said.

"Not here," Jupe stated. "None of these are fur."

And they were not. They were only plush and felt.

The woman who owned the shop was puzzled when Jupe told her they were searching for a fur bear. "Real fur," he said. "Mink, probably."

"That's sort of special," said the woman. "Does it have to be mink?"

"A dark fur," said Jupe. "A friend of ours had one, and I was wondering if she got it here."

"No. You could try the shop in Santa Monica – the one across from the pier. They have some really expensive toys. If they don't have a mink bear, they might know where you could get one."

The boys took the bus to Santa Monica and found the shop near the pier. It was called The End of the Rainbow, and in addition to bears and bunnies of all sizes and materials, it had hundreds of objects with hearts on them, or rainbows, or sometimes hearts *and* rainbows.

There were no mink teddy bears, however. The young woman who was in charge of the place recommended that the boys try some of the shops in Beverly Hills.

"They go for mink in Beverly Hills," she said. She gave them the addresses of a few toy stores on Beverly Drive and several more on Little Santa Monica.

They thanked her and straggled out to the street. After waiting a moment for a maroon Audi to pass, they crossed the street to the bus stop. Pete collapsed on the bench there.

"You realize this may take the rest of our lives," he complained.

"Maybe not," Jupiter answered. "I see a gold-plated Rolls-Royce in our future."

14

The Fuming Furrier

Worthington was free. He came with the Rolls and whisked the boys to Beverly Hills, where he parked in a loading zone on Beverly Drive.

"I shall stay with the car," he said. "If I must move, I will simply drive around the block."

Two women strolled past the car, one reading a guidebook. "Listen to this," she told her companion. " 'Beverly Hills is one of the most expensive communities in the country. Homes of highly-paid stars in the entertainment industry are tucked among the rolling hills. The shopping district . . .' " Glancing back at her friend, she froze in mid-sentence.

"Thelma!" she shrieked. "Would you get a load of that car!" She whipped out her camera and snapped a picture.

Worthington pretended not to notice. The woman was still gaping when the boys walked away.

There were two toy shops in the block where Worthington had parked. At the first one the boys had no luck at all. At the second, however, a slender man in leather pants reported seeing a mink bear.

"Not really for sale though," he said. "One of our customers got it as kind of a premium. She bought a fur jacket at the shop on the corner of Wilshire and Olympic. When the jacket was delivered, there was a bear with it. A little thank-you for patronizing the store."

"Ah!" said Jupe.

"I suppose you could buy a bear from the furrier, if you really must have one."

"Thank you," said Jupe.

"No trouble. Come back if you ever need a mouse house. I have some lovely mouse houses."

"For mice?" said Pete.

"Toy mice," said the man. "We don't allow live mice in Beverly Hills. Strict zoning, you know."

Pete snorted.

The boys went back to the car. They found Worthington explaining to a pedestrian that the Rolls was not a prop for a film. The chauffeur seemed relieved to see the Three Investigators. As he drove them towards Wilshire and Olympic he remarked that the area near Beverly Drive was becoming a tourist haunt.

"I had my photograph taken several times while you were away," he said. "People seem to think I'm an actor."

"You have to admit," Bob told him, "the car and your uniform look a little unusual – even for Beverly Hills."

"Perhaps you have a point, Master Robert," Worthington admitted, chuckling.

The shop at the corner of Wilshire and Olympic was called Vronsky Frères. The store had pearly grey walls and ankle-deep grey carpeting. When the boys arrived, a harassed man with a tape measure around his neck was fussing at a sullen young man who was vacuuming.

"Teddy bears?" said the man when Jupiter asked about Lucille Anderson's toy. "I used to have some bears. Right now I'm out of them. They were taken too."

"Taken?" said Jupe.

"In the break-ins," said the man. "You don't know? No, of course not. Why should you know? Two more burglaries are not news these days."

Jupe felt a little thrill. "Burglaries? When?"

"They took my furs the first time. That was a week ago. And then four nights ago they stole some records. Why? What's it to you? If you need a bear, go to a toy shop."

"But it's a fur bear our friend had," said Jupe "I think it was mink. We were keeping it for our friend, and someone broke into our house and took it."

The furrier nodded. "Like this place. They took the bears too when they got me the first time. But then they had to come back and wreck my files. Threw them all over the floor. I still can't find some of them. It's bad enough to lose the furs, but at least they were insured. Those crooks didn't

78

have to mess up my records too. Just nastiness. They want to show their contempt for people who work hard and get ahead.''

"Yes, sir," said Jupiter.

The young man with the vacuum cleaner unplugged the machine and disappeared into a back room. "That one!" The furrier nodded after him. "Maybe honest, maybe not. You can only hope. At least he does the work. The one before him, a hopeless case. I ask him to do something and I might as well go to the cemetery and dig up a dead man. I would get the same kind of service. He knew all about movies and nothing about work.''

Jupe thought he would explode. He felt Pete stiffen behind him. Bob leaned toward the furrier, careful not to miss a word.

"Your last helper was a movie buff?" said Jupe. "Did he know a lot about horror films?"

"How did you guess? Dracula! The Wolfman! Things that get out of graveyards and eat people. Awful stuff!"

Suddenly the furrier drew back, suspicious. "You knew my last helper? Wh-what's going on here? Who are you, and what do you want?"

"We . . . are trying to help find our friend," Jupe told him carefully. "The friend who had the mink bear. She's disappeared. It's terribly important. Please, how did you find this employee? Did an agency send him?"

The furrier scowled. "He just walked in. He said he needed work and he would do anything."

"Did he come before the burglaries, or after?" said Jupe. "And when did he leave? How long did he work here?"

"Not two days. I didn't keep him around at all. I fired him just over two weeks ago. Not that it's any of your business."

"The man's address?" Jupe persisted. "Where does he live? What name was he using? There's a Mrs Fowler – a woman who lives in Cheshire Square out in Rocky Beach. Is she a customer?"

"Now you want to know about my customers?" said the

furrier suspiciously. "This is no good. I'm calling the police!"

"Please, it's very important!" Jupe poured out the story of the runaway girl who lived with Mrs Fowler, and of the tote bag the boys had found. He told of the frantic parents. "We think the girl has been kidnapped, and it has something to do with the fur bear."

After hearing the story, the furrier was still suspicious. He admitted that he knew a Mrs Fowler but would not confirm that she was a customer. When pressed about his former employee, he grudgingly went into the back room and returned with some papers.

One was an official form that employers file with the government, giving the name and social security number of an employee. This one had been filled out by a person named Frank Jessup. The furrier showed Jupiter another sheet of paper on which Jessup's name and address were written by hand.

"I mailed the no-good his cheque," said the furrier.

"Was it returned by the post office?" Jupe asked.

"No."

"And what did this Jessup look like? Was he thin, with straight fair hair worn long, over his ears?"

"No. Short, kind of tubby, and dark hair. Curly dark hair. Look, I don't like this and –"

"Just one more thing," pleaded Jupe. "Where do the teddy bears come from? You don't make them yourself, do you?"

"No. I get them from a dealer. R.J. Importers."

"And you gave one to Mrs Fowler, right?" prompted Jupe.

"Out!" ordered the furrier.

As the boys left the shop, they could hear the furrier dialling the telephone.

"Calling the police," guessed Pete.

Jupe was unconcerned. He stepped to the kerb, where a maroon Audi had just pulled away, and started to cross the street to Worthington and the Rolls. "I think we can safely assume," he announced with satisfaction, "that Mrs

Fowler has at some time received a fur garment and a mink bear from Vronsky Frères, and that Lucille borrowed the bear after Mrs Fowler left for Europe. Now let's proceed with the case of the lazy creep-show fan."

"Did you get the address of that Jessup guy?" Bob asked.

"It's a side street in Santa Monica," said Jupiter. "There was an apartment number, so it must be in an apartment building."

"Probably as phony as the name," said Pete.

Jupe smiled. "Not necessarily. The furrier mailed his cheque to him, and the cheque didn't come back. Someone in Santa Monica received it.

"So the next step is to find out who it was. Lucille's life may depend on it!"

15

The Collector

"It might be better if everyone in Santa Monica doesn't know we're here," said Jupe.

"We do seem to have attracted a great deal of attention today, Master Jupiter," said Worthington. He pulled around a corner on to a side street. "We are now approximately three blocks from the address that the furrier gave you," he said. "I will wait here if you wish to go the rest of the way on foot. And you need not hurry on my account. I have a copy of the London *Times* and will be quite well occupied."

The boys went off down the street and around the corner. They walked past small apartment buildings and modest homes until they came to a garden court about ten blocks from the ocean. Apartment 15 was on the gound floor towards the back of the court.

Pete hesitated. "What do we do now?"

"We ring the bell," Jupe decided.

He did. There was no answer.

After a minute or two Bob put his face to the window. He could make out a room that was a jumble of books and papers and shabby rattan furniture. Several film cans and what appeared to be a skull sat on top of a bookcase. On the wall above the skull was a poster of a black-clad creature with a green face. The creature was stepping out of an open grave.

'Third Annual Convention!' was lettered above the ghoulish character in the poster. 'Horror Fan Club of North America. August 14 and 15, Santa Monica Civic Auditorium!'

"We've certainly got the right address," said Bob.

"You boys!" called a voice from the front of the garden court.

The boys turned. They saw a tall red-haired woman.

"You looking for Mr Morell?" she asked. She seemed to be the manager.

"Or his friend, Frank Jessup," said Jupe. He felt the same excitement he had felt when the furrier had mentioned horror films.

"Jessup? Don't know him. Mr Morell added that name to his letterbox for a few days, though. Mr Morell hasn't been home for a while. Must be on holiday. Want to leave a message? I'll see that he gets it. Or that other one – Jessup."

"Uh, thanks," said Jupe, and he took a notebook from his pocket.

The woman shook her head. "I never did see Jessup. Must've been staying with Mr Morell for a few days. Like Mr Pelucci does sometimes."

"Mr Pelucci?" Jupe could feel himself trembling now, he was so eager. They might be closing in on the phony Craig McLain at last. "Would that be the man with straight fair hair? The one who wears it kind of long, down over his ears?"

"Right. Iggy Pelucci."

"Iggy?" Jupiter asked. "That's short for Ignatius, right?"

"Yeah," said the woman, growing restive. "So you want to leave a message for Mr Morell or what?"

Jupe scrawled in his notebook, "Call Edward Hyde, 555-6359." He tore off the page and handed it to the woman. "I've got some old movie posters I found in my dad's garage," he said. "I want to see if Mr Morell wants to trade with me. Maybe I could call him where he works if you have the number."

"He's not working right now," the woman told him. "He used to work for a studio someplace until a few weeks ago, but they must have laid him off."

She looked at Jupe with curiosity. "So you're one of them, too?" she said.

"One of them?" said Jupe.

"Those horror freaks," said the woman. "Henry Morell has a whole bunch of weird stuff. His apartment's full of it, and his garage, and he rents an extra garage from me so he can store even more stuff there. He puts his car on the street. I think he doesn't eat sometimes just so he can buy more pictures and old bones and things. Don't waste your life. You're still young.''

A telephone rang somewhere in the building. The woman excused herself and went to answer it.

"So Morell is a collector," said Jupe. "We should have guessed. And his friend Iggy Pelucci stays with him sometimes. If Pelucci is the one who used McLain's name, we are really making progress!''

"So do we call the cops?" Pete wanted to know. "Or do we stake out the place? If Morell is a collector, he'll be back sooner or later. Collectors always come back for their stuff, don't they?''

"I believe so," said Jupe. He looked behind the U-shaped building that framed the court. Across an alley, he saw a row of garages, older ones with padlocks on the doors. Jupe drifted towards them, too curious to resist. He was just about to put his eye to a crack in one of the doors when a stocky, dark-haired man came into the back alley through a gate.

Jupe started.

Pete said, "Oh, no! It's Morell!"

It was indeed the curly-haired man who had been at Lucille's party with the phony Craig McLain. He recognized the boys and for an instant he stood still. Then he recovered his composure and came forward.

"So we meet again," said Morell. "What brings you here?''

"Lucille Anderson," said Jupe quietly. "Or Arianne Ardis, if that's the name you prefer.''

"Wha-what about her?''

"She's disappeared," said Jupe, "as you know very well. The man who calls himself Craig McLain –''

"Old Craig?" Morell tried to grin carelessly. It didn't work. "What about Craig?''

"His name is not McLain," said Jupiter. "Now if you would like to tell us where he is, perhaps we can talk. If not . . .''

84

At this point Pete lost his temper. He seized Morell's arm. "Don't try to fool us!" he said. "Where is the guy? And where is Lucille Anderson?"

"I don't know what you're talking about," said Morell. He was sweating now. "Listen, get your hands off me or I'll call the cops."

"You do that!" said Pete. "That would be super!"

"Uh, I m-mean," stumbled Morell, his little eyes darting furtively. "Listen, McLain is . . . he's got some pull in this town. And as soon as we get a few details ironed out, the cameras will roll. Lucille, uh, Arianne, is a raw talent. She needs forming, shaping. So we've set up some lessons for her – voice, acting, you know. We'll add lustre to her talent, give her some polish like a rare jewel."

Morell's face suddenly lit up. "Walk this way," he told them. "You've got a treat in store."

The boys gave each other incredulous looks.

Morell dug a bunch of keys out of his pocket and opened the padlock on one of the garage doors. "The old props!" he said. He sounded as if he were talking about sacred relics. "Feast your eyes! You remember the sequence in *Blood Harvest* where the zombie entered the castle? Look – there's the door that swung open when certain notes were played on the organ. And over there is the coffin from *Village of the Cursed*. And I managed to get my hands on some of the genuine wax figures from the first picture about the wax museum, even the very make-up that Lon Chaney used in *Phantom of the Opera*! Not to mention prints of the original films – and a cache of the old scripts!"

"It's . . . it's like a museum!" said Bob. In spite of themselves, the Three Investigators had followed Morell into the garage, and they stood gaping in wonder at the gruesome objects all around. Jupe was especially fascinated with a poster in a frame. It advertised the movie *Frankenstein*, featuring Boris Karloff, and it was in perfect condition. For half a century or more, it had been cared for as if it were a rare painting.

After a moment, Jupe turned to say something to Morell

but Morell was gone. The Three Investigators had been left in the middle of a jumble of ancient movie memorabilia.

"Morell?" called Jupe.

There was no answer. Suddenly the garage door swung shut and the boys were in darkness.

"Hey!" yelled Pete.

The boys heard a lock rattle into place on the outside of the door.

"Hey, Morell!" Pete floundered through the gloom towards the door, where tiny cracks of light showed. "Hey! Open up!"

He pounded and he shouted. Outside the garage it was silent. Henry Morell was gone, and the boys were locked in!

16

Chamber of Horrors!

"Somebody has got to hear!" Bob's voice was high and shrill. He pounded on the garage door. "Hey! Hey, out there!"

No one answered.

After yelling for a few more minutes, the boys gave up.

"If only we hadn't let the Rolls park out front," said Pete bitterly. "How long will it take before Worthington comes to look for us? And will he think of looking in this garage?"

"We can't wait for Worthington," said Jupiter "Suppose Morell comes back and brings his friend. They could be armed!"

Pete made a moaning sound. "I wish you hadn't thought of that," he said.

"We have to find another way out of here," Jupe decided. "There could be a window someplace. They used to put windows in garages. And if there is one, it would be at the end of the building. I think we're in the second stall from the end. If there isn't a solid wall, we might be able to walk through."

"And if not," said Bob, "what then?"

"Then we bang some more," Jupe told him. But he was already squinting into the shadows, trying to see a path through the heaps of old props. His hand grazed metal instruments of torture. He shuddered and began to move away from the door, groping in front of him, touching steel, leather, and a rubbery substance – what must have been costumes. He could make out fright masks and wigs and cans and jars and bottles.

Out of the semi-darkness vague silhouettes of distorted figures menaced the boys. Even more frightening were the blurred shapes they could not make out at all, but could only imagine. A rank smell enveloped them – the smell of old things imprisoned too long in a small space.

Bob and Pete shuffled along behind Jupe. After they had gone deeper into the darkness, they felt Jupe stop and heard him gasp.

"What is it?" whispered Bob.

"Something's here," Jupe whispered back. "Something really awful!"

Jupe was feeling the thing that was in his way. He touched a hard smooth surface, then he felt fur, and then a mouth. And teeth. Fangs, really.

Jupe bent forward, his hands exploring the awful thing, his eyes getting used to the shadows now.

The thing that crouched there was half ape and half human. After a few moments, Jupe was almost sure he knew what it was.

"Remember those monsters that came out of the caves in the movie *Nightmare Island*?" he said. "I think this is one of them."

"How would Morell get hold of it?" said Bob, trying to sound matter-of-fact. "I didn't know studios ever sold their stuff."

"Who cares?" Pete put in. "Let's get out of here!"

He tried to edge past the horrible thing. Suddenly he stopped. It was beginning to move. There was a grating whine. The menacing creature straightened, lifted its long arms, and staggered toward them, clanking. The hungry mouth opened and shut as if the thing were chewing.

In a far corner of the garage something squeaked and scuttled. The boys found themselves clutching each other.

"Rats!" Pete managed to say, shuddering.

Jupiter cleared his throat before he could assume his normal voice. "They won't bother us," he said bravely. "Rats are only dangerous if you corner them, and we couldn't corner anything in here."

"I wonder why I don't feel reassured," Bob said sarcastically.

The mechanical monster had stopped its whining and clanking. It stood in their path, long arms still reaching up, and they knew they could not move it. They would have to find a way around it.

"We can shift some of those cartons," said Pete, and he set to work. Bob and Jupe pitched in, sweating and panting. Soon the boys had opened a passageway to the beams that separated one garage stall from the next. Pete was the first to step through into the cleared area of the next stall. As he did so he ducked, choking, his hands flailing at the air.

"What is it?" whispered Bob.

"Cobwebs! Agh!" Pete was making sweeping motions with his arms.

Suddenly he felt something more substantial than a cobweb. His hand met a cord of some kind that was stretched across the open area. He took hold of it and gave a cautious tug.

A scream erupted – pitiful, eerie as a banshee cry. Something flew out of the darkness, brushed past Pete's face, then vanished.

Pete yelled and dodged.

"Holy cow!" gasped Pete. "The place is booby-trapped. I think that was a mechanical bat."

Bob tried to laugh. "Morell must have ransacked a fun house too," he said.

Now the boys could dimly see another barrier ahead of them. It was a wall made of coffins, which stood on end against the garage wall. From behind them came a gleam of light.

"Great!" exclaimed Jupe. "There *is* a window!"

Now things stirred and rustled overhead, and the boys could hear scampering in far corners, but they did not care. They were nearing freedom – and fresh air!

Pete started to tug coffins out of the way. Bob and Jupe helped, dragging the heavy objects away from the window. As the boys worked, only a little more light came into the garage.

At last the boys could see the window. Morell had nailed boards across the opening on the inside, but he had done a hasty, careless job. The boys could look out between the boards and see a little side yard where oleanders grew.

Pete yanked at a board, but he couldn't budge it by himself. When Bob and Jupe took hold and all three of them pulled at once, it came away from the window with a screech.

And there was more light in the garage.

The second board that Pete attacked broke in his hands, and he pushed it aside. The third and fourth boards gave way immediately.

Pete shoved the window open and put his head out. Instantly he had the feeling that someone was hovering by him.

He turned his head. There stood a police officer with a gun in his hand.

"Oh, boy!" said Pete.

"Come out quietly and no funny business," said the officer.

His partner was there too, on the other side of the window. He watched, grinning a bit, as Pete scrambled out. Bob came after him. Jupe was last, trying to be as dignified as he could.

The red-haired manager of the building was standing nearby. "Yes, those are the kids," she said. "They was asking questions about Mr Morell. When I heard yelling in his garage, I thought it could be them. How'd you get in there anyway?" she demanded of Jupe.

Ignoring her, Jupiter addressed the policemen. "I wish to file a complaint," he said. "We were imprisoned by Henry Morell."

"Uh-huh!" said one of the officers. His face was stony.

"Mr Morell's been away for days," said the manager.

Jupe stood very erect and spoke in a calm, measured voice. "A girl is missing," he said. "Her name is Lucille Anderson. As far as we know, Henry Morell and a companion were probably the last to see her. That was yesterday at Cheshire Square. We suspect that Morell and his companion spirited her out past the security guard there, either hiding her in the boot of their car or perhaps in the back seat. She may have been covered with a rug or a coat to prevent the guard from seeing her."

"You watch a lot of TV?" asked one of the officers.

"You can verify my story," said Jupe. "Call Chief Reynolds in Rocky Beach. He is investigating Lucille Anderson's disappearance, and he knows us."

An older man, a man who looked both weary and patient, came around the corner of the building. A younger man was with him. The two newcomers were not in uniform, but it was clear that the officers knew them. The police officers stepped back respectfully to let them talk with Jupiter.

Jupe quickly realized that they were plainclothes detectives. He guessed that they had been contacted by the furrier who had been robbed.

The detectives listened as Jupe told his story again. Once they realized that there might be a connection between the stolen furs and the missing teenager, they listened more intently.

The older detective told the boys to wait, then he vanished for a time. The uniformed officers went off with the manager to verify that Henry Morell was not at home. Eventually they returned. The Three Investigators were warned about poking into things that did not concern them, and about trying to beat the police at apprehending criminals. The senior detective wrote down the boys' names and addresses, and then he let them go.

A group of curious neighbours had gathered around the squad car parked in front of the building.

"Hey, mister!" said a toddler on a tricycle. "Did the cops catch some bugglers?"

"Not exactly," said Jupiter.

The three boys hurried away from the crowd, heading back towards the place where Worthington waited with the car. Halfway down the block Jupe noticed a maroon Audi parked at the kerb. As the boys neared it the driver turned his head away as if he were looking for something that had fallen down on the far side of the passenger seat.

"Oh!" said Jupe. He hesitated for a fraction of a second, then walked on, looking straight ahead.

"What?" said Bob. "Did you just see something?"

"Don't look back," said Jupe. "A man was sitting in that car we just passed – and he could watch Morell's building from here."

"So?" asked Bob. "Half the neighbourhood is out watching Morell's building. What about it?"

"I could swear I've been seeing that maroon Audi all day. And I'm almost positive that the driver is Mr Sears from the Pizza Shack in Rocky Beach. He was pretending not to notice us. And he was trying to keep us from noticing him. What could he possibly be doing here?"

17

A Plunge into Peril

The boys found Worthington standing between the Rolls-Royce and a crowd of neighbourhood children who had come to stare at the car. The chauffeur brightened at the sight of the Three Investigators. He hurried to open the rear door of the car so that they could get in.

"Where to, young gentlemen?" asked Worthington.

"A telephone box," said Jupiter. "We are going to track some teddy bears to their den." Jupe wanted to question the wholesaler who supplied the furrier with his fur teddy bears.

Jupiter had Worthington stop at a petrol station and checked the telephone directory at the pay phone. The address of R.J. Importers was a street in Long Beach, about a forty-five-minute drive south.

"Having established the connection between Morell and the furrier, and the furrier and the bears, and the bears and Lucille, it seems appropriate to investigate the place that supplied the bears to the furrier," said Jupiter.

"It is out of our usual territory," said Worthington. "I have a street atlas, however, and we shall find it."

He set out and the boys in the back seat began an excited discussion about the teddy bear that had been in Lucille's tote, and about the ones that had been stolen from the furrier along with his furs.

"Drugs!" declared Bob. "What else could it be but drugs? The guy in Long Beach is an importer, and the drugs are shipped in from South America or Asia. They're hidden in the bears so the customs inspectors don't find them. By mistake, a shipment of bears containing cocaine or heroin or whatever is forwarded to that poor guy in Beverly Hills, so Morell and his pal have to intercept the bears!"

"But if the bears are mink, your story doesn't work," said Pete. "I have an aunt who has a mink coat. She told me

93

that most minks come from Canada. Heroin doesn't come in through Canada, does it? Or cocaine?''

"One thing we can be sure of," Jupe declared. "There is more involved here than a toy!"

"But what's in the bear, Jupe?" Pete insisted.

The First Investigator tried to look knowing and kept silent.

R.J. Importers turned out to be a long, low building on a dingy street near the waterfront in Long Beach. It looked grimy and deserted, with no lights in the windows and no lorries parked beside it.

Again it seemed wise to have Worthington park the Rolls out of sight. He promised to wait for the boys at a small restaurant a few blocks away, near the main road. Then he tipped his cap and drove off.

Bob stood scowling at the front of the building, which faced west towards the ocean. "What do we do now?" he said. "It doesn't look as if there's anyone there."

"We knock and find out," Jupiter told him.

"So if somebody comes to the door, what do we do?" Pete wondered. "Tell them we want to buy a teddy bear?"

"Why not?" said Jupe. "We can say Mrs Fowler has one, and we traced it here and want one for a present for . . . for Aunt Mathilda."

"Your Aunt Mathilda wouldn't be caught dead with a mink teddy bear," said Bob.

"So long as the importer doesn't know Aunt Mathilda, we are safe," said Jupe.

He went up two steps to the door and knocked. No one came to open the door, and no one stirred inside the building. Through the glass panel in the top of the door he saw a bleak little office that was neat and empty.

"So much for that." Jupe turned away from the door and looked around.

On the north side of the building was an empty car park. The boys straggled into this and looked up at windows that had iron grilles over them. Pete spotted a wooden crate on the ground near the rear of the building. He got the crate, put it under a side window, and stood on it to look in.

"Well?" said Bob.

"It looks like some kind of a big stock room," Pete told him. "There's a lot of steel shelving with stuff on it. Bears! I see some bears. And dolls, and things in cartons. There's a big table with a roll of brown paper, and there's packing stuff and a roll of labels. There's just the one big room with some office space, I guess, partitioned off at the front. Oh, and one of the back corners is partitioned off from the rest. There's a little square room in the far back corner. It could be the washroom. No. No, the washroom is up front next to the office. There's a sign on the door."

"Maybe the little room is where they keep the drugs, or the jewels, or whatever they stuff inside the bears," Bob guessed.

Pete got down off the box and picked it up. "Maybe we can look in from the other side and see," he said.

But when the three boys went around to the back of the building, and then on to the south side of the place, they found that there were no windows that would give them a view into the small corner room Pete had noticed. It had been partitioned off in a blind corner.

"It must be black as pitch in there," said Bob.

"Jewels!" said Pete. "Drugs! All locked up!"

"Shhh! Listen!" warned Jupe.

A car had stopped in front of the place, out of sight. The boys heard the car engine, and then they heard the engine die. A car door slammed, and someone went up the front steps to the door of the building.

"Aha!" Bob muttered softly. "Now we can do our act. We can go in and try to buy a bear for Aunt Mathilda."

But when they peeked around the corner of the warehouse, they froze, dumbstruck.

A maroon Audi was sitting at the kerb. It looked exactly like the car that had been parked on the street where Henry Morell lived.

The boys retreated.

"Here's an unexpected turn of events," said Jupe. "Could that be the man who was watching Morell's place today? Or was he watching us? And is it really Mr

Sears – the guy who runs the Pizza Shack? Or was I mistaken?"

"We'll watch until he comes out," said Bob. "Sooner or later he's got to come out."

They waited, sheltered behind a small van that was parked a short distance down the street. Fifteen minutes passed, and then twenty, and then the door of R.J. Importers opened. A man came out carrying a duffel bag. He put the bag into the boot of the Audi, then got into the car and drove off.

"Would you get a load of that!" exclaimed Pete. "It *is* that Sears guy! He's probably the boss of the whole operation. And we were sitting in his pizza place blabbing our heads off about Lucille and the teddy bear and – no wonder he's following us!"

"We've got to get in there!" cried Bob. "There must be some evidence in there! Or . . . hey, Lucille could be in that little locked room!"

"The cops!" said Pete. "We call the cops and they get a warrant and go in and get her out."

"I don't think they can," said Jupe. He sounded discouraged. "They can't get a warrant without a really good reason to believe there is a crime going on. What do we have to tell them? This man owns a pizza parlour where we talked about Lucille? And he seems to own this building, or at least have access to it? That isn't evidence. It's hardly enough to make anyone suspicious!"

"Wait a second!" Pete snapped his fingers. "Skylights!" he said. "There are skylights in that roof. I saw them when I looked in the window. If there's a skylight over that hidden room, we could look right down into it."

Pete started for the back of the building, and Jupe and Bob followed. There was a loading bay near the far corner, close to the car park. Pete scrambled up on to the loading bay. From there he grabbed a drain-pipe that was fastened to the corner of the building, and shinnied up on to the roof.

"Don't try to go in," called Jupe. "There may be alarms and you don't want to get trapped."

"And hurry!" said Bob. "If anybody sees us here, we

won't have to call the cops. They'll come whether we want them or not!''

"I hear you," said Pete, and he headed across the roof. The roof was flat, and the skylights stuck up at regular intervals. There were six of them, and Pete saw with a thrill that one had to be over the enclosed little room in the back corner of the building.

He went to the skylight, knelt, and looked down. At first he saw nothing. The room below was shadowy, with only the single opening in the roof to let the light in. And the skylight was streaked with grime.

Pete made a fist and rubbed at the gritty glass. The he saw that there were iron bars inside the skylight.

He put his face down to the glass and framed his eyes with his hands. Squinting, he could just make out bare walls and a bare cement floor and heaps of dark objects that looked like bulging sacks.

"What's there?" It was Jupe who was suddenly beside Pete. The chubby boy had scrambled up to join his friend. Pete did not answer him, but moved to one side so Jupe could look for himself.

"What do you suppose all that is?" Jupe said after a minute or two.

"Beats me."

Jupe sat back on his heels. "At least we know Lucille isn't shut in there. Not that that means we are any nearer to solving our case. Toys! Mr Sears imports toys! Or is he merely connected with an importer? Do Morell and McLain work for him? Did Lucille discover some sinister secret about the toy in her tote?"

The boys stayed where they were for several minutes, with Jupe trying frantically to think of some clue he might have overlooked – some answer to the riddle.

"Hey, you guys!" It was Bob calling from the alley. "Hey, are you okay?"

"We're coming," said Jupe. He stood up and started across the roof towards the drainpipe.

Suddenly the worn old timbers in the roof gave a threatening groan. Jupe stopped.

"Stay right there!" warned Pete. "Don't move!"

He dropped to his knees to better distribute his weight, then crawled towards the parapet that ran around the edge of the roof. "I'll find a board or . . . or something you can put across the roof and . . ."

Jupe sneezed.

"Don't do that!" Pete had one leg over the parapet.

Jupe sneezed again, hard. It threw him off balance. Without thinking, he took a step back.

The roof groaned again, and then it gave way.

Jupe's hands clawed for a hold he never found. His face frozen in alarm, he plunged through the rotten timbers!

18

Nowhere to Hide

Jupe lay in the darkness and tried to breathe. At first he could not. He struggled, rolling on to his side, and the breath came at last in a great gulp.

"Jupe? Jupe, are you okay?"

It was Pete. He had edged as close as he dared to the hole in the roof. He lay flat now, looking down.

"Jupe?" he called again.

"I'm here. I'm okay." Jupe got to his knees. Then he stood up, leaning on the wall next to him. It was the wall that enclosed the hidden room. He had fallen into the main room just beside the door to the small one.

"Jupe, be careful," pleaded Pete.

"Right." Jupe reached out and tried to turn the doorknob. It wouldn't turn. He shoved against the door, but nothing gave. The door was very solid, and very securely locked.

Jupe looked around at the steel shelves that filled the place. He saw fur teddy bears, little horses, and dolls with painted smiles. There were boxes of blocks and cartons of yo-yos – toys were everywhere.

Jupe went to one of the shelves and took a fur bear. It looked just like Lucille's. With the bear in his hand, he started towards the front of the building – towards the partition that separated the office from the warehouse.

The door in the front partition opened easily. Jupe looked into the office and saw a couple of desks. He crossed to the front door of the building and was about to open it when he heard a car come down the street.

Jupe peeked through the glass panel in the door. The maroon Audi was slowing to a stop!

Jupe turned and fled back into the warehouse, closing the office door behind him.

On the roof, Pete shifted his weight. "Jupe, where are you?"

The call was soft – hardly more than a whisper.

Jupe ran across the warehouse and looked up at the hole in the roof. "Get down from there!" he told Pete. "That guy's coming back!"

Pete scrambled away from the hole. Jupe heard him cross the roof and then climb down the drainpipe at the back of the building. Sneakered feet hit the loading bay, and Jupe grinned. Pete was safe.

Jupe crouched behind a stack of cartons as a key rattled in the door beyond the partition. Someone came into the office. Jupe heard casters roll on the bare linoleum floor as a chair was pulled out. Then the chair creaked as someone sat down. Drawers opened and papers rustled and a man cleared his throat.

What was Sears doing? Had he come back to catch up on some paperwork? Would he be at it for a long time?

Jupe looked to the back of the huge room. Double sliding doors there led out to the loading bay. He could get out that way . . . if he could unlock them. Or he could take a desperate chance. He could hide and wait, and perhaps Sears would leave without coming into the main room of the warehouse. He might not find out about the hole in the roof – and Jupe might still have a chance to discover the secret of the locked room.

Jupe stepped into the shadows behind a bank of loaded steel shelves and waited.

Not for long. Suddenly the chair was pushed back in the front room. There were footsteps. The man was coming. In a second he would open the inner door to the warehouse. He would look in.

He would see! He would see the hole in the roof and the debris on the floor. He would know!

Jupe looked towards the doors that led out to the loading platform. Could he make it?

He could not. The office door opened suddenly and Jupe ducked down behind the rows of teddy bears and the eternally smiling dolls. He peeked between the shelves and saw Mr Sears' torso as he came in. He heard the footsteps on the dusty floor.

Sears stopped before he had gone a dozen paces. He bent slightly forward. He had seen the splintered wood and the shreds of tar paper on the floor.

Jupe saw Sears' hand. It disappeared under his suitcoat. Then he saw the gun. The grey-haired man must have drawn it from a holster under his coat. Now he held it ready as he took several quick steps towards the crumbled mess on the floor.

Jupe crouched lower. If Sears kept going, he would soon be past. The way would be clear for Jupe. He had to escape before Sears began searching. It would take him only a second to get out from behind the shelves and get to the office door. He could be through that door and out of the front door in a flash. Once he was on the street, he would be safer. Outside Sears would not dare to shoot. Jupiter could run and run. He could find Worthington and safety.

He heard a siren. It was not far away. The man in the warehouse heard it and was uneasy. He stood without moving, the gun held ready. When the sound had faded into the distance, Sears started forward again.

Now! It had to be now! Did Jupe dare?

Then a miracle happened. Someone pounded on the front door of the building.

The man with the gun jumped. He hesitated and the pounding came again. "Hello in there!" cried a hearty voice. "Anyone there? I say, I need some help!"

Sears turned and went out to the office. "Who is it?" he called.

"I'm terribly sorry to bother you, but I'm lost!" came the voice from the street. "I say, can you tell me where I can find Carter's Machine Parts?"

"Across the street and down the block," answered the main in the office gruffly.

"But I couldn't see any sign there," said the cheerful wanderer on the front step. He sounded quite willing to stand and discuss the location of Carter's until the cows came home. Jupe did not wait. He stole out from behind the shelves of toys and made straight for the doors to the loading platform at the back. Mercifully, the bolt barring the

101

doors shot back easily and quietly. Freedom! As Jupiter inched open one door he could just barely hear Worthington. The chauffeur was still babbling about the difficulty of finding addresses in an unfamiliar neighbourhood with insufficient signs.

Jupe grinned as he squeezed out on to the loading bay and silently closed the door behind him.

The Rolls-Royce sped north.

"Worthington, you were great!" exclaimed Jupiter.

Worthington nodded. "I pride myself on being of service, Master Jupiter," he said.

"We figured you could run into some trouble," said Pete. "We saw it was Mr Sears again. We thought that the guy might recognize us if we went to the door, but he couldn't know Worthington. So what happened? Did you find out anything?"

"Not really," Jupe confessed. "The man has a gun and he might have used it. But that really isn't significant. Many people have guns."

Jupe still had the teddy bear in his hand. He was examining it now, poking at the seams. "Odd," he said. "It's not soft like the usual stuffed toy. If feels as if there's wood or plastic under the fur."

He tugged the head a little, wondering if it would come off.

"It is a small safe, Master Jupiter," said Worthington. "One of my clients has a similar toy. The mistress of the house is supposed to place jewels in the bear and then sit the bear out in plain sight on her bed. Many adults have stuffed animals on their beds, and it excites no special interest. The burglar ignores the bear and goes away empty-handed."

Pete hit himself in the head. "For the love of . . ." he groaned. "We should have asked you at the very start."

"The head unscrews," added Worthington.

It did. But when Jupiter looked inside the body of the little creature, he saw nothing but an empty plastic cavity.

"No drugs," he told Bob. "No smuggled jewels. Nothing at all. Sorry."

Bob threw himself back against the seat, and Pete scowled. "You mean we're back to square one?" Pete complained. "Some guy who is made up like Dracula's pet ghoul comes busting into Headquarters and knocks you out and makes off with the bear. It was probably Morell, who knows all about Dracula. So why? There had to be something in Lucille's bear. There just had to be something to make it all worth that. And there has got to be some tie-in with the bears that were stolen from the furrier. Morell was mixed up in that one, I bet!"

"Master Jupiter, do you wish to notify the police?" Worthington asked.

Jupe hesitated. "If we did that, what could we tell them?" he said at last. "We don't really know much more than we did when we talked to those detective a few hours ago at Morell's apartment. Only that by a peculiar coincidence the man who owns the Pizza Shack in Rocky Beach also seems to own the toy warehouse where Lucille's bear originated. That isn't a crime, is it? It really could be a coincidence."

Worthington nodded. "Too true," he said, and he did not speak again for the rest of the drive to Rocky Beach.

The sun was just setting when the Rolls drove up in front of The Jones Salvage Yard. The iron gates at the entrance to the yard were closed for the day. Uncle Titus stood in front of them, however, obviously watching for Jupe and his friends.

"You should have called," he scolded. "Your aunt has been worried."

"I'm sorry, Uncle Titus," said Jupe. "We were . . . we were in a place where we couldn't call. And then I forgot the time."

"As long as you're safe," said Uncle Titus. "Don't go off again and be gone all day without letting us know. And I want to ask you something. I've been thinking . . . Do you think our robbery had something to do with the girl at Cheshire Square?"

"It may have, Uncle Titus," said Jupe.

"I just don't want him coming back to pester Mathilda,"

his uncle told him. "You don't like feeling that it's not safe to turn around in your own kitchen."

"There's nothing to worry about now," Jupiter reassured him. "The thief got what he was after and won't be back."

"In that case," Uncle Titus said, grinning, "you'd better say good night to your friends and wash up before your aunt skins you alive!"

19

Jupe Plays a Hunch

Jupiter woke during the night. He heard footsteps on the street outside, and the sound of someone singing a mournful old song. Something about poor little lambs that had lost their way, baa, baa, baa; little black sheep who had gone astray . . .

Jupe lay in bed, annoyed at the singing, and wondered if he'd have to count sheep before he could fall asleep again. His mind drifted . . .

Suddenly he sat up in bed. Sheep! Little lambs! That was it! The clue to help him find Lucille's abductors!

He squinted at the clock on the bedside table. It was three in the morning. He could not possibly call Worthington. Or Pete or Bob. Not at three in the morning. And not just to test a theory. Besides, there was little anyone could do until it was light.

Jupe lay down to wait for the dark, silent hours to pass. He dozed and woke and dozed again. When at last it was light he got up and dressed and ate breakfast.

At seven thirty he called Bob.

"Remember what McLain said when he met Lucille's parents?" he asked.

"He said he'd put Lucille in pictures," answered Bob.

"Not that. He said he was staying at a place that used to belong to Cecil B. DeMille, and that there were sheep grazing nearby."

Bob said nothing. Jupe could hear him yawn.

"The remark about Cecil B. DeMille is the sort of thing a phony would say to impress people," Jupe continued. "He wanted the Andersons to think he was rich and important. But sheep? I don't think he would make up a detail like sheep grazing nearby. Bob, wherever McLain – I mean, Pelucci – was staying, there were sheep around. Where do you find sheep in the Los Angeles area?"

"Beats me," said Bob. "Early in the spring you sometimes see them grazing on the hillsides along the coast, but then they're transported up to the Sierras or somewhere like that."

"Right," said Jupe. "They ship them to places where it's cooler so the wool will be good. But there must be some left around here somewhere. Listen, there might be an old house or an abandoned barn up in the hills where a couple of guys could hide out – a place with sheep grazing nearby. It's only been three days since Pelucci made that remark, so the chances are good that the sheep are still there."

"Okay," said Bob. "So what are we waiting for?" He sounded alert and eager now.

"Worthington," said Jupe. "If he isn't engaged today, I think he'd like to be in on this."

"I'll call Pete," said Bob. "You call Worthington!"

Worthington arrived at The Jones Salvage Yard before nine. He was not driving the Rolls. Instead, he was at the wheel of a jacked-up Jeep with huge wheels.

"The Rolls seemed inappropriate for this expedition," said Worthington primly. "This vehicle belongs to a friend of mine who spends his weekends at something he calls off-road driving. I do not understand why one would leave a good road to go jouncing through the rough countryside, but he appears to enjoy it. The vehicle does have some things to recommend it, however, such as four-wheel drive."

"Worthington, you're super!" Bob exclaimed.

"I try my best, Master Robert," the chauffeur replied.

The boys got into the vehicle. Worthington shifted gears, and they were off at a pace that was more breakneck than usual. They headed up the Pacific Coast Highway and then turned off on a narrow track called Cottonwood Creek Road. Worthington shifted again and the borrowed vehicle climbed the steep grade with hardly a groan. The boys watched the countryside right and left as they went.

They came out on to Mulholland Highway before fifteen minutes had passed. Mulholland ran along the crest of the mountains from Hollywood almost to Ventura, and at first Worthington headed back towards the city, since there would doubtless be more houses in that direction.

Jupe had binoculars, and he used them to scan the hills above the road and to search the grassy fields in the canyons below. Once the boys spotted a biker pedalling along, sweating and staring ahead with intense concentration. Worthington pulled to one side and Jupe hailed the biker, who stopped even though he obviously did not want to.

"We're looking for a friend," said Jupe. "A man who's tending sheep somewhere in the hills. There's been an emergency in his family, and we need to get in touch with him."

"Sorry," panted the biker. "Haven't seen anybody."

They drove on. A mile or two down the road Jupe saw grey lumps on the slope above the main road and thought they were rocks. Then one of them moved and he knew they were not rocks – they were sheep. Next he saw a battered van and a man beside it sitting in a folding chair and playing a harmonica.

"There they are!" said Jupe.

He pointed. Worthington looked quickly and then pulled his vehicle over on to a stretch of hard shoulder. The boys got out and hiked up the incline to the man in the pasture.

"We're looking for some friends," Jupe called when they were close enough to be heard. "Two men and a girl. They were staying at a place here in the hills, and we don't have an address."

Bob looked around. As far as he could see, there was no sign of a house – not a roof nor a chimney nor a lane running off the main road.

"One of our friends said they could hear sheep where they were staying," Jupe kept on as the shepherd continued to stare at him. "I haven't seen houses near here. Are there other flocks of sheep in the hills now?"

The shepherd shrugged. "I have not seen any," he said. He had a slight European accent. "Maybe if you go west along the road you will have some luck. Until last night my flock was a mile or two back that way, below the road."

Jupe thanked him, and the boys returned to Worthington.

"West," said Jupe. "He was grazing the sheep west of here. In a pasture below the road. We may have to take this vehicle off the road yet, Worthington."

"We can do it, Master Jupiter, never fear," replied the chauffeur.

They made a U-turn and headed back the way they had come. Soon they were beyond the place where Cottonwood Creek Road intersected Mulholland, and they went more slowly.

The hills seemed just as empty on this stretch of the road. Rocky Beach was only a few minutes away, but the boys might have been in a wilderness.

Then, less than a mile past the intersection, a grey stone tower could be seen below the road, rising behind a clump of trees. As Worthington drove closer, stone walls showed below the tower, topped by battlemented parapets.

"It's a castle!" cried Pete.

Worthington stopped the car in sight of a rutted dirt road that ran from the main road down to the castle.

"Look! There's a fort, too!" said Bob, pointing to one side of the castle. The fort consisted of several log cabins surrounded by a high stockade fence.

"And there's an old western town," added Pete, staring at some false-fronted wooden buildings that lined a dusty little street on the other side of the castle.

"That's it!" exclaimed Jupe. "That's the place!" His eyes were shining. He had followed his hunch and it had paid off.

"But . . . but that isn't a real place," Pete objected. "It's just an old movie location!"

"Exactly!" said Jupe. "If you're a phony like Pelucci, you would never admit to anyone that you didn't have a fancy home – especially if you were hiding out in an abandoned movie location after ripping off a fur shop. Instead, you might say you were staying temporarily at a place that used to belong to Cecil B. DeMille.

"Let's just hope that our fake producer and his creepshow pal are still here – and that they have Lucille!"

20

Escape to Nowhere!

"Worthington, you wait here," said Jupiter. "If we run into trouble and it looks as if we can't handle it, go for help."

"You may count on me, Master Jupiter," said Worthington.

The Three Investigators went down the boulder-strewn slope, avoiding the road in case Morell and Pelucci might be watching. They approached the old film location from the side, through scattered brush. The place was a jumble of shabby sets connected by an empty dirt street. In addition to the castle, fort, and western town, there were houses of different historical periods and a New England church with a steeple. Most of the buildings were no more than flimsy shells, with walls on only two or three sides and the interior exposed to weather.

Like most movie locations, this one had been changed around from time to time. Buildings had been added to or altered. Houses had been moved or partly dismantled. The set for the town of the Old West was still fairly intact. The boys saw signs for a general store, a saloon, and a sheriff's office and jail in the two rows of buildings.

The whole place was very quiet.

"Where do we start looking?" whispered Bob.

It was not easy to decide. Jupe let his gaze wander through the forlorn little place. He reasoned that Morell and Pelucci, if they were camping out here, would prefer a building that was fairly weather-proof – which meant one that had a floor and four walls and a roof. The building that was supposed to be the jail looked quite sturdy and complete, and so did the general store. The log fort also appeared substantial, as did the castle and the church.

Jupe decided that the castle was a likely place to start their search. It looked almost solid enough to be made of real stone, and there were barred windows in the grey walls. Even if Morell and Pelucci were not camping out in it, they might have shut Lucille in behind the bars.

Jupe pointed to the castle and then started forward. The other two boys followed him. When they were nearer, they saw that a door in one of the walls had a shiny new padlock on it.

"That's it!" whispered Bob.

Jupe motioned for silence.

The three searchers crept close and peered in through a barred window. They saw a vast shadowed space inside. The floor was made of wide wooden planks, and a shapeless mass of something lay nearby. It looked as if someone had thrown down a heap of dark fabric and left it to moulder away there.

"Lucille!" Jupe called softly. "Lucille, are you there?"

The mass of fabric stirred and moved. Lucille Anderson sat up. Her face was very white in the gloom, and her eyes were very dark.

"Lucille, it's Jupiter Jones," said Jupe. "My friends Pete and Bob are with me. Where are Morell and Pel – I mean, McLain?"

The girl untangled herself from a cocoon of blanket and sleeping bag, got up, and came stumbling to the window. She was wearing the dark skirt and white blouse that she had worn when the boys first saw her. The blouse was streaked with dirt and her hair was matted and tangled. Her feet were bare.

"We'll get you out," Jupe promised. He was still whispering.

She whispered back, "Be careful. I think they're crazy."

"Where are they?" Jupe asked again.

"Up there. In the general store."

Jupe nodded, and he and Pete began to work on the bars that covered the window. Bob raced up the slope to the road to ask Worthington to go for the police.

Like most things in that artificial place, the bars that imprisoned Lucille were intended for show rather than for use. They were made of wood, not steel or iron. When Bob

110

came back down the slope, Pete and Jupe were working the nails out of the frame that held the bars in place. Inside the castle, Lucille had begun to cry.

"Crazy!" she kept saying. "They're crazy. Really! All this over a stupid toy!"

"The teddy bear?" said Jupe. "That's what they wanted, isn't it? And they got it. Why?"

"I don't know. I had just got out of the bath when they came to Mrs Fowler's house and said they wanted to talk with me about the Dracula picture. It was a lie. I was talking to Henry down in the living room and Craig went upstairs. He said he was just going to the kitchen to get a drink of water, but instead he went upstairs. I could hear him up there, and I began to wonder, and so I went up after him. Henry tried to stop me but I went up anyway. Craig was in Mrs Fowler's room and he was opening the bureau drawers. He wanted to know about the teddy bear and . . . and he grabbed my arm and said I had to tell him."

She broke down again and sobbed. "He said I had to tell him . . . or else. I ran into the bathroom and tried to lock the door but he shoved it open and he . . . he hit me. My nose began to bleed and he didn't care. He just twisted my arm until it hurt and I told him the bear was in the tote bag and you . . . you probably had it and . . ."

"It's all right," said Jupe. The nails had been stubborn at first, but with the help of the screwdriver on his Swiss army knife they were coming loose.

"I thought once they knew about the bear, they'd go away and leave me alone, but they didn't."

"They were afraid you'd call the police," said Jupe. "I can guess the rest. They hid you in the car and brought you here."

"The boot of the car," she said. "Henry had a gun. He said he'd shoot me if I made any noise."

The last nail came out. Pete gripped the wooden bars with both hands and pulled.

The bars came loose with a soft scraping noise. Lucille made a leap and the boys helped her scramble out through the window. Her long skirt caught on something and held for a second, but she yanked at it and ripped it free. Then they were all hurrying, running from the castle, headed for the slope that went up to the main road. Lucille was careless of her bare feet. She did not seem to notice pebbles and burrs on the ground.

And then the door of the general store opened and Henry Morell came out into the sunlight. He was carrying a paper plate with some food on it. When he saw the boys and Lucille he froze for a moment. Then he shouted, "Iggy! Iggy!"

The boys ran faster. Pete had Lucille by one elbow. Bob held the other and urged her along. Once she stubbed her toe and almost fell. She gasped with pain, but she did not stop.

There was an old English cottage in the path of the Three Investigators. The front door was open, and the boys sped through with Lucille hopping beside them. They slammed the door and then scooted through the house and out of the open rear. Then they dodged along the back of a row of sets, and finally got in through the window of the little church.

They knelt on the floor. Bob peered out cautiously through a crack in the front wall of the building.

Morell and Pelucci were both on the street now, and both had guns. The two would-be movie moguls looked desperate. They knew they had to recapture Lucille, or she would turn them in for kidnapping. To make her a prisoner again, they would also have to capture the three boys. And what then? Were the two desperate enough to do away with all four of the young people?

Bob saw Morell and Pelucci go the length of the street. The men looked into doorways as they went. Then they started back. This time they searched more carefully.

"Rats!" said Bob. "They're coming this way. They'll find us for sure!"

The boys looked around, searching for a way to escape. But there was none. If they made a run for the main road, the two men would see them and shoot. They would have to hide.

Pete was the one who spotted the tiny bell tower. There were no stairs up to it, but the boards nailed at intervals to the wall studs could serve as a ladder. Lucille and the boys could get up into the tower – and maybe the searchers wouldn't see them.

They heard the two men now. They were calling to each other as they stamped through the empty sets. Doors were banged open. Once there was a shout when Iggy Pelucci saw a snake.

Lucille shuddered, but she kept still. Bob took her hand and urged her towards the makeshift ladder on the wall. She went without hesitation, gathered her long skirts with one hand, and climbed onto the platform halfway up the bell tower. The boys followed her.

There was hardly enough room on the platform for all of them, but they managed, flattening themselves against the floor so they would not be seen from below or through the tower windows.

Now the searchers were in the fort across the way. . . . Now they were in the colonial house next door. . . . And now the boys heard the church door open. Footsteps clomped loudly on the wooden floor.

Suddenly a scuttling, squeaking sort of noise came from above. Something was up there in the bell tower – something hidden in the deep shadows just under the roof. They heard the faint flap of wings. Bats!

Lucille looked up. Her eyes widened and she looked ready to scream. Jupe reached out to silence her.

But Lucille did not scream. She only let out a choked whimper.

It was enough. The man in the church below held still for barely a second. The he crossed the floor. His footsteps were hard and hurried. He stood under the belfry and looked up. When he spoke, his voice was quiet and controlled.

"Come on down," said Henry Morell, "or I'll pump you full of lead."

Jupe wanted to laugh. Morell was as corny as an old movie. But he had a gun. Jupe kept quiet.

113

"Come down, I say!" Morell shouted now. "I know you're up there!"

The boys might have moved, but they heard another sound. It was faint at first, but it swelled and grew louder. It was the sound of car engines roaring and horns blaring. And then there were shouts above the roars.

Beneath the belfry, Morell stepped back, nervous and wondering. He crossed to a window.

Pete rose to his knees and peeked out through one of the tower windows.

"Unreal," he breathed.

"What?" whispered Bob. "What is it?"

Before Pete could answer, they heard Morell downstairs. He was running out of the church. On the street outside Pelucci was shouting for him to come quick.

Pete watched Pelucci sprint across the dusty street to the fort. The man threw open the great log gate and raced to the shabby grey sedan parked beyond the stockade. Morell was close behind. In seconds the sedan was rolling out through the gate.

The Investigators and Lucille scrambled down from the bell tower and ran outside. The grey sedan was well down the dusty street now, making for the road that led up to the main road. Then the sedan stopped short as a caravan of rumbling, roaring, souped-up and stripped-down cars came hurtling into view.

The lead car in the caravan might once have been a normal Ford. Now it sparkled with purple paint, and painted green flames danced all along its sides. The twin tailpipes rumbled and the huge tyres threw up dust and rocks. Behind the purple monster came a rusty, battered vehicle with no top. It was overflowing with teenagers. Four boys who were obviously sturdy, well-muscled surfers shouted when they saw the grey sedan, and one of them beat on the side of the jalopy with a fist.

"Haaah-yiahh!" yelled a girl who drove a little Volkswagen Beetle that was painted orange. The three boys with her all looked ready for action. The Toyota behind the VW was also loaded with young people who yelled loud threats. Last in the procession came Worthington in his Jeep. He was accompanied by the waitress from the Pizza Shack, who had armed herself with a rolling pin.

At the wheel of the grey car, Pelucci saw that he could not possibly get up to the main road in time. Any moment the army of angry teenagers would be on the dirt track that led down to the movie sets. But the man was desperate to escape. He gunned his engine.

The sedan took off with its back wheels throwing dirt. It skidded into a U-turn that sent it heading out away from the main road – out towards the open slopes beyond the movie location. The car swerved around a flagpole, barely missed the open gate of the fort, and sped past the Investigators at the church door. Then it was jouncing into sagebrush and over boulders as Pelucci tried to cross the rugged hillside.

For a few moments he managed. But then he came to a huge boulder. Pelucci yanked at the steering wheel, trying to get around it. One wheel climbed the great rock and one spun on loose earth. The engine roared and the car tilted at a crazy angle. Then the wheels were turning in empty air and the car slid sideways, half off the boulder and half on.

The sedan crunched to a stop, the frame broken.

Pelucci and Morell struggled out. The two men staggered across the hill, still trying to flee. But the angry teenagers were out of their cars now and running.

Morell turned at the last second. He lifted the gun in his hand. Then the surfer at the head of the posse threw himself at Morell's legs, and the older man went down. The gun bounced away.

Pelucci simply sat down and let the teenagers pile on to him. It was over at last, and he knew it!

21

Worthington Comes to Tea

Hector Sebastian returned from Idaho a week after the rescue of Lucille Anderson, and Jupiter called him immediately.

"We've just concluded a case," he said. "How would you like to hear about it?"

"By any chance would it have something to do with a teenage girl from Fresno?" said Mr Sebastian.

"How did you know?"

"Just a hunch you guys were behind the headline story in the papers," the writer told him, chuckling. "How about tomorrow around four? Come for tea. Don is serving tea these days."

Jupiter hesitated, wondering if he could suggest a round of colas instead.

"You'll like the tea," coaxed Mr Sebastian. "Trust me."

"All right," Jupe answered. "Can we bring a couple of friends?"

"Is one of them a teenager with theatrical ambitions?" asked Mr Sebastian.

"She promises she won't ask you to get her a part in pictures," said Jupe. "She just wants to meet you. Worthington is also a fan of yours. He has all of your books."

"Oh, great! I've always wanted to meet Worthington. Bring him along. Or let him bring you."

Jupe grinned and hung up. Then he dialled the Fowler house and also Worthington.

The chauffeur appeared promptly at half past three the next afternoon. He was driving the fabulous gold-plated Rolls, but he was not wearing his uniform. Instead he had on grey slacks and a blue blazer. "Today I am a guest, not a chauffeur," he announced. "I thought I should dress appropriately."

"You look great, Worthington," said Pete. "I wonder what get-up Lucille will have on."

"I bet it'll be something flashy," Bob predicted. "She'll want to knock Mr Sebastian dead!"

But when Lucille came out of the Fowler house to get into the car, she was dressed simply in slacks and a cotton blouse.

"Lucille!" cried Pete. "Who are you this afternoon?"

"Can't you tell?" she said dramatically. "I'm just being me. I've had it with costumes."

They drove north on the Coast Highway, and when they turned on to the canyon road where Mr Sebastian lived, Lucille sat forward, watching for Mr Sebastian's house. She spotted it at last.

"Hey, he really did keep the neon lights that were on the place when it was a restaurant. I thought you guys were kidding me."

"Nope," said Bob. "He uses them, too. He puts them on at night for guests who don't know the way. They outline the house in pink."

When the car pulled up in front of the house, Mr Sebastian came out on to the porch. Hoang Van Don, his houseman, followed close behind, beaming at the guests. Don seemed especially impressed by Worthington. He bowed and bowed to the Englishman, then suddenly popped back into the house as if overcome with shyness.

"Don has been very excited since he learned you were coming today, Worthington," said Mr Sebastian. "He has been watching a lot of British shows on television, and now that he can meet a genuine Englishman in person, he feels his life is complete. He's been getting ready all day. Wonderful smells are coming from the kitchen."

"My word!" said Worthington.

The screenwriter then smiled at Lucille and offered his arm to escort her into the house.

There had been changes in the big airy living room since the Three Investigators had last seen it. The patio table and the canvas director's chairs that were usually by the fireplace had been replaced by chrome chairs and a huge chrome and glass coffee table. And the screenwriter had

117

added a beige rug that looked bumpy and expensive.

Pete whistled in admiration.

"Do you like it?" asked Mr Sebastian. "A friend convinced me that I needed some real furniture in here, and she ordered this stuff for me while I was out of town. It's fancier than the old patio furniture, but it somehow leaves me cold. I want something I can put my feet up on."

He motioned to his guests to take seats. "Now, tell me what you've been up to," he said.

Bob cleared his throat and summarized the Investigators' recent adventure, occasionally referring to some notes he'd brought along. When he got to the grand finale – with Worthington and the teenagers – Mr Sebastian burst out laughing.

"Why in the world did you bring those kids instead of the police, Worthington?" asked Mr Sebastian.

Worthington permitted himself a chuckle. "I had to drive all the way back to the Coast Highway before I found a telephone," he explained, "and the first public instrument I tried was out of service. I continued down the main road until I located a working telephone – which happened to be in the Pizza Shack. Some of Miss Anderson's friends overheard me talking to the police and offered to help. We managed to arrive back at the film location just before the police. I must say," the chauffeur added, "I enjoyed the rescue thoroughly."

Everyone laughed.

"Now, what about that bear?" asked the screenwriter. "The one Lucille was abducted over. What was so important about it?"

"Wait till you hear this!" said Lucille.

"Jupe found the bear while the police were arresting Morell and Pelucci," said Bob. "He realized he'd seen that castle before."

"It was used in an old horror film called *Prisoner of Haunted Hill*," Jupe explained. "And I remembered a scene in which the master of the castle opens a secret panel in the wall and finds a wizard's crown. I was sure Morell and Pelucci knew that scene, too."

"So Jupe marches into the castle, walks into a little room, puts his hand on a wooden panel, and – whammo – the panel opens!" Pete said. "And there's Lucille's bear!"

"Good work, Jupe," said Mr Sebastian. "But what was in the bear? Drugs? Diamonds? The suspense is killing me!"

"I'm sorry to disappoint you," said Jupe with a smile, "but there was nothing in the bear but money."

"Money?" echoed the screenwriter. He looked puzzled. "Was it counterfeit?"

"Oh, no," answered Jupe. "It was real – and in large denominations. Morell and Pulucci stole it from Sears."

"You mean they weren't all working together?"

"Not at all," said Jupe. "The story is, Morell and Pelucci were two dreamers who were wild about movies. But somehow they couldn't break into the business. Morell had been a messenger at Globe Studios, but he got fired. Pelucci sometimes worked as a movie extra, but that wasn't enough for him. The two of them decided to become independent film producers. They thought that all you needed to become a producer is an idea and some money, and Morell had the idea. Make a sequel to *Dracula*."

"It's been done a number of times," said Mr Sebastian dryly.

Pete grinned. "Maybe that's why nobody would give them the money to make the picture."

"By chance," Jupe went on, "Pelucci found a job as a shipping clerk in Mr Sears' toy import firm, which was mostly a mail-order business. He became curious about the locked room in the warehouse, the one we never got into. One day he swiped Sears' keys and went into the room and found sacks and sacks of money. He stole a sack, but knew he couldn't just walk out with it, so he stuffed wads of bills into some teddy bear banks that were being shipped to a furrier. The box went out by United Parcel Service, and Pelucci never showed up at the warehouse again.

"Morell now got a job with the furrier so he could retrieve the money from the teddy bears. But he was so inept that he was fired before the bears ever arrived. So then Morell and Pelucci burgled the store and stole fur coats as well as the bears. They sold the coats to a fence and emptied out the bear banks. But one of the bears was missing – the one that got sent to Mrs Fowler – so they had to break into the store again to get the furrier's records and find out who had the bear.''

"They couldn't just forget about that one bear?" asked Mr Sebastian.

"No way – it had ten thousand dollars in it!" said Pete. "And they needed every penny they could get to finance their Dracula movie."

"Now we come to the part of the story that we were involved in," said Jupe. "Morell broke into Mrs Fowler's place, looking for the bear, and found Lucille instead. He and Pelucci struck up an acquaintance with her in Rocky Beach – she wasn't hard to recognize with that Victorian costume – convinced her that they were movie producers, and threw the party for her as a way to get into the house and search for the bear. It wasn't there, of course; it was back at Headquarters. So the next day Pelucci and Morell grabbed Lucille and forced her to tell where the bear was, and Morell broke into my house and then Headquarters."

"Wearing that silly monster costume," added Pete in disgust.

"But didn't they dress up like that a lot?" asked Mr Sebastian. "Didn't they hold up the pawnbroker and the off licence dressed like creatures out of horror movies?"

"No," said Bob. "That was some *other* loony! He's held up a couple of other places since Pelucci and Morell were arrested. Whoever he is, he gave Morell the idea of using a monster costume for his own hold-up. Nothing these guys ever did was original."

Mr Sebastian laughed. "And now for the rest of the story. What was Sears doing with all that cash? And why was he following you boys around?"

"Because he heard us talking about Iggy and teddy bears at the Pizza Shack," said Bob. "He thought maybe we could lead him to Iggy Pelucci, who had stolen his money and disappeared."

"Why didn't Sears just call the police?" asked the screenwriter.

"He couldn't risk disclosing the theft," said Jupe, "because apparently he's in the business of laundering money."

The screenwriter smiled. "Ah, I thought it might be something like that!"

"I don't get this part at all," said Lucille. "What's laundering money?"

"That's when you take 'dirty' money – cash profits from illegal activities like drug dealing and gambling – and find a way to make it 'clean' and legitimate," explained Mr Sebastian.

"Why not just put the money in the bank?" asked Lucille.

"If only it were that simple," said Mr Sebastian. "Let me explain. Banks are required to report cash transactions of ten thousand dollars or more to the U.S. Treasury Department, which might then check into the source of the money. They're always trying to spot drug dealers. But they aren't particularly concerned about money that comes from a regular business that takes in a lot of cash, like a restuarant or supermarket."

"And that's what Sears owned – a bunch of small businesses that dealt in cash," said Bob. "The Pizza Shack, a dry cleaner's, a bowling alley. The police don't think Sears was a drug dealer himself – he just laundered money for dealers. All he had to do was mingle the illegal profits of his clients with the regular cash income of his businesses, put everything in his own business bank accounts, even pay taxes on it, and then find a way to get his clients' money back to them. Minus his cut, of course."

"The police also think that Sears carried a lot of his clients' money abroad on his many toy-buying trips," said Jupe, "and deposited it in secret Swiss bank accounts."

"And what does Sears have to say to all this?" asked Mr Sebastian.

"Nothing. He's disappeared!" said Pete. "Probably skipped the country."

"Meanwhile Morell and Pelucci are in custody for burglary and kidnapping," said Jupe. "They blabbed everything they knew about Sears, hoping for lighter sentences, but they didn't really know much. They couldn't name the big-time criminals who were Sears' clients. So Pelucci and Morell are still in big trouble. Lucille will testify against them, of course, and some of the furrier's records were found in Pelucci's car, which is very incriminating."

"They ended up producing a horror story after all – a real-life one for themselves!" said Mr Sebastian.

A door opened on the far side of the living room, and the screenwriter sat up expectantly. "Ah, here comes Don. Now you're in for a treat."

The Vietnamese houseman came across the room carrying a huge tray. He put it on the table in front of Mr Sebastian and said, "Proper English tea, like gentlemen and ladies have in afternoon. You like tea!"

It was indeed a proper English tea, with the teapot kept warm by a tea cozy; an extra pot of hot water to dilute the tea; cream and sugar and lemon; and plates of toast and watercress sandwiches and some crispy-looking buns and little cakes with coloured frosting.

"I make buns myself," Don told them.

"Splendid!" said Worthington happily. "I haven't seen the like since I came to America. Good show, Don."

Don smiled and bowed himself out.

Mr Sebastian asked Lucille to pour the tea. Pleased, she immediately assumed the role of an English lady and poured as if she'd been doing it all her life. The Investigators didn't much care for the tea and ignored the watercress sandwiches, but ate everything else. Worthington happily finished the sandwiches himself.

And then Lucille made a dramatic announcement. "I am going back to school!" she said. "I went home to Fresno with Mum and Daddy for a couple of days and we talked and talked, and we worked it out. I'll stay with Mrs Fowler and help out, like I'm doing now. But I'll give up my job at the Tender Touch and finish high school in Rocky Beach.

"Then I'm going to try for one of the really good drama

schools. And let me tell you, I'm never going to borrow a teddy bear from anyone ever again!"

"Sounds like a good plan," said the screenwriter. "And a lot less hairy than your recent adventures," he added with a twinkle in his eye.

Everyone groaned.

Then the last little cake was gone and Worthington was looking at his watch. The visit was over. Worthington and Lucille walked out to the car while the Three Investigators lingered briefly with Mr Sebastian.

"I like Lucille better now that she's acting like a normal person instead of some kind of imitation movie star," Pete admitted.

Mr Sebastian chuckled. "Enjoy it while you can. Once an actress, always an actress. By next week she may be Lady Macbeth or the Bride of Frankenstein."

"Give me a break," Pete protested. "I've had all the creep shows I can take!"

Nancy Drew Mystery Stories

Nancy Drew is the best-known and most-loved girl detective ever. Join her and her best friends, George Fayne and Bess Marvin, in her many thrilling adventures available in Armada.

Armada

The Hardy Boys Mystery Stories

Frank and Joe Hardy are the most famous young detective team ever. Join the brothers and their friends in these fabulous adventures.

Armada

Have you read all the "Secrets" stories by Enid Blyton?

THE SECRET ISLAND

Peggy, Mike and Nora are having a miserable time with unkind Aunt Harriet and Uncle Henry – until they make friends with wild Jack and discover the secret island.

THE SECRET OF SPIGGY HOLES

On a holiday by the sea, Mike, Jack, Peggy and Nora discover a secret passage – and a royal prisoner in a sinister cliff-top house. The children plan to free the young prince – and take him to the secret island.

THE SECRET MOUNTAIN

Jack, Peggy, Nora and Mike team up with Prince Paul of Baronia to search for their parents, who have been kidnapped and taken to the secret mountain. Their daring rescue mission seems doomed to failure – especially when the children are captured and one of them is to be sacrificed to the sun-god.

THE SECRET OF KILLIMOOIN

When Prince Paul invited Nora, Mike, Peggy and Jack to spend the summer holidays with him in Baronia, they were thrilled. By amazing luck, they find the hidden entrance to the Secret Forest – but can they find their way out?

THE SECRET OF MOON CASTLE

Moon Castle is said to have had a violent, mysterious past so Jack, Peggy, Mike and Nora are wildly excited when Prince Paul's family rent it for the holidays. When weird things begin to happen, the children are determined to know the strange secrets the castle hides . . .

Armada

'JINNY' BOOKS
by Patricia Leitch

When Jinny Manders rescues Shantih, a chestnut Arab, from a cruel circus, her dreams of owning a horse of her own seem to come true. But Shantih is wild and unrideable.

This is an exciting and moving series of books about a very special relationship between a girl and a magnificent horse.

FOR LOVE OF A HORSE
A DEVIL TO RIDE
THE SUMMER RIDERS
NIGHT OF THE RED HORSE
GALLOP TO THE HILLS
HORSE IN A MILLION
THE MAGIC PONY
RIDE LIKE THE WIND
CHESTNUT GOLD
JUMP FOR THE MOON
HORSE OF FIRE

Armada

Armadas

Here are some of the most recent titles
in our exciting fiction series:

The Chalet School and Rosalie *Elinor M. Brent-Dyer* £1.75
The Secret of the Forgotten City *Carolyn Keene* £1.95
The Masked Monkey *Franklin W. Dixon* £1.95
The Mystery of the Creep-Show Crooks *M. V. Carey* £1.95
Horse of Fire *Patricia Leitch* £1.75
Cry of a Seagull *Monica Dickens* £1.75
The Secret of Moon Castle *Enid Blyton* £1.95
Legion of the Dead *J. H. Brennan* £1.95

Armada paperbacks are available in
bookshops and newsagents, but can
also be ordered by post.

How to Order

Please send the purchase price plus 22p per book (maxi-
mum postal charge £3.00) to Armada Paperbacks, Cash
Sales Dept., GPO Box 29, Douglas, Isle of Man. Please use
cheque, postal or money order – do not send currency.

NAME (Block letters) ....

ADDRESS ....

....

....